11+ English

When it comes to 11+ preparation, nothing beats practice — and this CGP book is packed with the best practice you'll find, all at the perfect level for ages 10-11.

It starts with questions that focus on one topic at a time, so children can really get to grips with each key skill. Once they're confident, there's a selection of mixed-topic Assessment Tests to help them get used to the style of the real 11+ papers.

We've also included detailed, step-by-step answers. Everything you need!

How to access your free Online Edition

This book includes a free Online Edition to read on your PC, Mac or tablet.
You'll just need to go to **cgpbooks.co.uk/extras** and enter this code:

4270 4412 8906 6212

By the way, this code only works for one person. If somebody else has used this book before you, they might have already claimed the Online Edition.

Practice Book – Ages 10-11
with Assessment Tests

How to use this Practice Book

This book is divided into two parts — themed question practice and full-length assessment tests. There are answers and detailed explanations at the back of the book.

Themed question practice

- Each page contains practice questions divided by topic. Use these pages to work out your child's strengths and the areas they find tricky. The questions get harder down each page.

- Your child can use the smiley face tick boxes to evaluate how confident they feel with each topic.

Assessment tests

- The second part of the book contains six full-length assessment tests, each with two comprehension texts and a matching set of questions. Each test also includes a set of questions on grammar, spelling and punctuation. They take a similar form to the real test.

- You can print multiple-choice answer sheets so your child can practise the tests as if they're sitting the real thing — visit cgpbooks.co.uk/11plus/answer-sheets or scan the QR code.→

Answer Sheets

- Use the printable answer sheets if you want your child to do each test more than once.

- If you want to give your child timed practice, give them a time limit of 50 minutes for each test, and ask them to work as quickly and carefully as they can.

- The tests get harder from 1-6, so don't be surprised if your child finds the later ones more tricky.

- Your child should aim for a mark of around 85% (43 questions correct) in each test. If they score less than this, use their results to work out the areas they need more practice on.

- If they haven't managed to finish the test in time, they need to work on increasing their speed, whereas if they have made a lot of mistakes, they need to work more carefully.

- Keep track of your child's scores using the progress chart at the back of the book.

p.29: *Hag Storm* extract © Victoria Williamson 2021 reproduced with permission from Cranachan Publishing.

p.37: From *ESPERANZA RISING* by Pam Muñoz Ryan. Copyright © 2000 by Pam Muñoz Ryan. Reprinted by permission of Scholastic Inc.

p.53: Extract from *Out of Heart* Copyright © Irfan Master, 2017. First published in the UK by Hot Key Books, an imprint of Bonnier Books UK Ltd.

A note for teachers, parents and caregivers
Just something to bear in mind if you're choosing further reading for 10-11 year olds — all the extracts in this book are suitable for children of this age, but we can't vouch for the full texts they're taken from, or other works by the same authors.

Published by CGP

Editors:
Claire Boulter, Siân Butler, Heather Cowley, Robbie Driscoll, Rebecca Greaves, Georgina Paxman

With thanks to Emma Cleasby for the proofreading.
With thanks to Jan Greenway for the copyright research.

ISBN: 978 1 78908 803 8

Printed by Elanders Ltd, Newcastle upon Tyne.
Clipart from Corel®

Based on the classic CGP style created by Richard Parsons.

Text, design, layout and original illustrations © Coordination Group Publications Ltd. (CGP) 2022
All rights reserved.

Photocopying this book is not permitted, even if you have a CLA licence.
Extra copies are available from CGP with next day delivery • 0800 1712 712 • www.cgpbooks.co.uk

Contents

Tick off the check box for each topic as you go along.

Parts of Speech

Nouns

Write down whether the word in bold is a proper noun, a collective noun, a common noun or an abstract noun. For example:

> The **herd** of elephants charged across the plain.   <u>collective noun</u>

1. The vet observed the litter of kittens from a **distance**.   _____

2. People were shocked to see the swarm of flying **ants**.   _____

3. **Karim** saw ships approaching from across the bay.   _____

4. The flowers were starting to deteriorate in the **heat**.   _____

5. The professor's entire class gave him a standing **ovation**.   _____

6. There was only one **bunch** of keys on the table.   _____

7. A group of thieves ransacked the old village **hall**.   _____

8. The **band** approached the stage nervously.   _____

9. It's wonderful to hear a **congregation** singing together.   _____

/ 9

Underline the word in each sentence which matches the part of speech in brackets. For example:

> Greg walked <u>slowly</u> behind his sister.   **(adverb)**

10. The historian's precious vase fell onto the floor and smashed.   **(preposition)**

11. The students filed confidently into the classroom, prepared for their test.   **(adjective)**

12. Nobody could believe how rapidly the fire spread through the deserted building.   **(adverb)**

13. Although it was raining, a large crowd gathered outside the court.   **(preposition)**

14. Yan squeezed carefully through the narrow gap in the wall.   **(adverb)**

15. My grandfather takes his daily exercises seriously.   **(adjective)**

16. Grace put the handwritten note in her trouser pocket.   **(preposition)**

Hint: Check the glossary on p.77 if you're not sure of a technical term.

17. There were no clear signs of damage to the policeman's car.   **(adjective)**

18. Peter arrived late because he struggled to find his lucky socks.   **(adverb)**

/ 9

Parts of Speech

Conjunctions

Underline the most appropriate conjunction from the brackets to complete each sentence. For example:

The door will lock automatically **(<u>if</u> but although)** you shut it.

1. Mike attempted the high jump **(even though that so)** it was very ambitious.

2. Unfortunately, our battered suitcase broke **(before till if)** we departed for the airport.

3. Laura glanced outside **(why when unless)** she heard the parade passing.

4. My brother practised the music **(so since that)** he was ready for the performance.

5. The plants withered **(whereas unless because)** nobody watered them.

6. Ajay hurriedly explained **(so why unless)** the computer no longer worked.

7. The teacher had forgotten **(though because whether)** he had marked the assessment.

8. The girls slept soundly **(if since while)** the storm raged outside.

9. Many people enjoy jogging **(that whereas why)** I find it tedious.

/ 9

Clauses

Underline the clause in each sentence which matches the type of clause in the brackets. For example:

<u>Baljit ran home</u> because he had missed the bus. **(main)**

10. Although Emily enjoys football, she prefers netball. **(main)**

11. The chef prepared a casserole before the guests arrived. **(main)**

12. We left the arena when the announcement was made. **(subordinate)**

13. The lemurs escaped even though the enclosure was shut. **(main)**

14. Kristen detests walking unless she chooses the route. **(subordinate)**

15. Since I stopped biting my nails, they look much neater. **(main)**

16. Prisha waved frantically so that everyone could see her. **(subordinate)**

17. The tanker ran aground after it collided with the rocks. **(main)**

18. If anybody opens the front door, an alarm will sound. **(subordinate)**

/ 9

Verbs

Verbs

Underline the verb in each sentence. For example:

Ezra <u>found</u> a rusty key in the garden.

1. Every morning after breakfast, Reuben brushes his teeth thoroughly.

2. The children peered out of the filthy window at their neighbours.

3. In more than ten years, Amar never once missed the bus to school.

4. After the thunderstorm, the thick, grey clouds suddenly parted.

5. My eldest brother photographs the llamas and rhinos at the zoo.

6. There were only seven people on the beach on Thursday afternoon.

7. All of a sudden, Hayley heard a muffled shout from the gloomy cave.

8. According to my aunt, ferns thrive in wooded, shady areas.

9. At the sight of the enormous spider in the hall, Jill stifled a scream.

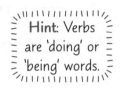

Hint: Verbs are 'doing' or 'being' words.

/ 9

Verbs

Underline the correct verb from the brackets to complete each sentence. For example:

I **(feels <u>felt</u> feeling)** sick on the rollercoaster.

10. The trees in the forest **(shaking shake shakes)** in the strong wind.

11. There **(is were was)** an elderly man waiting outside the bank when it opened.

12. The cat had **(fell fallen falls)** from the highest branch, but it wasn't injured.

13. The marble **(tumbles tumble tumbling)** down the long flight of stairs.

14. Harry **(was is are)** working at his desk when he heard the exciting news.

15. If you **(was were will)** to come to the party, what time would you arrive?

16. She **(has have had)** run three miles before her left knee started to ache.

17. **(Stop Stops Stopped)** playing football when you hear the referee's whistle.

18. I ask that you all **(remains remained remain)** seated until the ride stops.

/ 9

Verbs

Underline the word or words in each sentence which match the part of speech in brackets. For example:

The <u>postman</u> delivered the letters. **(subject)**

1. My uncle Arthur paints beautiful pictures. **(object)**

2. Shen developed a sore throat soon after he woke up. **(subject)**

3. Mrs Bartlett drives her car very slowly. **(object)**

4. After the competition, the presenter revealed the results. **(subject)**

5. During the lesson, pupils played the piano in pairs. **(subject)**

6. My cousins examined the document with interest. **(object)**

7. Aarvi spotted the cat through the hedge. **(object)**

8. Despite a previous bad experience, I visited the restaurant again. **(subject)**

9. The lawyer shouted loudly at the thief. **(object)**

Hint: The subject performs the action whilst the object receives the action.

/ 9

Rewrite each active sentence so that it is passive. For example:

The teacher wrote the angry letter.
<u>The angry letter was written by the teacher.</u>

10. The storm damaged the fence.

_____

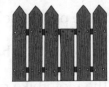

11. My dentist will fix my broken tooth.

_____

12. Our cat bit the dog's paw.

_____

Hint: For these questions, include the person or thing doing the action in your new sentence.

13. The police detained the angry driver.

_____

14. An earthquake shakes their house.

_____

/ 5

Section One — Grammar

Mixed Grammar Questions

Each sentence has one grammatical error. Underline the word which is wrong and write the correct word on the line. For example:

Hamid felt the bus <u>stops</u> suddenly.   _stop_

~~~~~~
 Hint: Read the sentence with your correction to check you have definitely fixed the error.
~~~~~~

1. You was about to explain the situation when I interrupted you. _____

2. That bright hat on the windowsill is your. _____

3. The children can't see no broken glass on the pavement. _____

4. The serving spoons is all in the same cutlery drawer. _____

5. The monkey had stole a piece of fruit from my pocket. _____

6. I refuse to tell you what of the answers is correct. _____

7. Mr Clarke told me that I can bring mine own calculator. _____

8. James did good in the chemistry assessment. _____

9. Kamil and me ran through the deserted streets to get home. _____

/ 9

Write down whether the word in bold is a noun, verb, adjective, adverb or preposition. For example:

The grey clouds **blocked** out the sun.   _verb_

10. Some people believe that it is difficult to measure **success**. _____

11. As she walked **briskly** to the concert, Kathryn smiled. _____

12. The motorbike raced **around** the corner and crossed the line. _____

13. The shopkeeper smiled **warmly** as he greeted his friend. _____

14. The **oily** stain spread over the tablecloth. _____

15. **Look** at that beautiful sunset over there! _____

16. Toby put his pencils **by** the exam paper and waited patiently. _____

17. The results were **better** than anyone could have predicted. _____

18. This month, our family **fasts** during the day and eats at night. _____

/ 9

Mixed Grammar Questions

Underline the word in each sentence which matches the part of speech in brackets. For example:

There are many beautiful streets in <u>Paris</u>. **(proper noun)**

1. Gradually, the hamster emerged from behind the wardrobe. **(adverb)**

2. Our teacher, Miss O'Neill, prided herself on her generosity. **(abstract noun)**

3. The detective signalled to them secretly with a small nod. **(pronoun)**

4. We can go bowling, unless you would prefer to play tennis. **(conjunction)**

5. Sophie leapt from the highest diving board without hesitation. **(verb)**

6. Nina told her cousin that she would be arriving late. **(common noun)**

7. Nobody can accurately remember what the winding street used to look like. **(adjective)**

8. The students usually became restless during the summer term. **(adverb)**

9. Strange noises could be heard at the abandoned property. **(preposition)**

/ 9

Underline the most appropriate word from the brackets to complete each sentence. For example:

Kevin had **(ate eat eats <u>eaten</u>)** the entire pizza.

10. Rosie took the **(large largest largely larger)** apple of all from the fruit bowl.

11. Fiona stroked the newborn lamb **(gentle gently gentlest gentler)**.

12. Carys **(doing done does do)** all the housework whereas John cooks every night.

13. The door slammed **(despite why what when)** the wind blew suddenly.

14. If I were you, I would **(avoided avoids avoid avoiding)** that street.

15. I told my parents that the late library books were **(me I mine my)**.

16. The snow fell **(steady steadily soft quiet)** during the night.

17. **(Although Why Yet Whenever)** the rain had stopped, it was very humid.

18. Casey and her family often **(go goes going gone)** skiing at Christmas.

/ 9

Section One — Grammar

Commas and Brackets

Brackets

Each of these sentences is missing a pair of brackets. Add brackets around the correct words in each sentence. For example:

> Our teacher (Miss Ryan) always has a tidy classroom .

1. One of my dogs the loud one has a habit of barking at squirrels .

2. A crowd of people 150 individuals were waiting to board the plane .

3. The singer dropped something important at the concert his microphone .

4. Ostriches birds that have extremely long necks can run quickly .

5. Sumaya plays sports football and basketball with her brothers and sisters .

6. Lia went on the slide many times at least ten before she went home .

7. Rachel finds tornadoes a type of extreme weather fascinating .

8. My grandad's house a small cottage is very cosy in the winter .

9. Someone not me dropped a bowl of tomato soup on the white carpet .

/ 9

Commas

Add one comma to each sentence so that it is correct. For example:

> Aliya, who is very funny, is always telling jokes.

10. The diver was mesmerised by the jellyfish dolphins and sharks.

11. To my dismay I fell in the puddle and got totally drenched.

12. Nick is planning an exciting trip to Cairo Egypt.

13. Despite her mother's protests Maya brought the snail inside.

14. Ikemba an avid reader, has read more than fifty books this year.

15. The cake which was fresh out of the oven, had mysteriously disappeared.

16. My spy outfit consisted of sunglasses, a dark shirt gloves and black trousers.

17. I usually take Gemma, my younger sister ice skating on Saturdays.

18. The forest dark and eerie, was feared by all who heard about it.

/ 9

Dashes and Hyphens

Dashes

Write down whether each sentence uses dashes correctly or incorrectly. For example:

> Timmy — who was hungry — ate all the food. _____correct_____

1. The puzzle nearly impossible to solve — took us hours. _____

2. Everyone froze — a growl had sounded from nearby. _____

3. The milk chocolate — my favourite melted in the sun. _____

4. I named my kitten — Shadow — she always follows me. _____

5. A cheer erupted from the stadium — the goal was amazing. _____

6. The baby — once settled in her cot — fell asleep. _____

7. The meadow looks lovely it's filled — with purple flowers. _____

8. Sea creatures — large and small — fascinate Annabel. _____

9. The best place — though it's small is my school's library. _____

/ 9

Hyphens

Underline the two words in each sentence that should be joined with a hyphen. For example:

> Mabel could not understand the <u>fast talking</u> parrot.

10. My class were badly behaved on a two day trip to the Lake District last summer.

11. Beatrice always shows up to hockey practice looking fresh faced and full of energy.

12. My brother Omar is the co author of a very popular series of crime novels.

13. Elias made a last minute dash to the shops to buy his mum a bunch of flowers.

14. Ryley packed his bag in preparation for an all inclusive holiday to Spain.

15. On her seventieth birthday, my grandma met her long lost twin.

16. Millie had to go to a French speaking school when she moved to France.

17. Tamara is the only blue eyed member of her friendship group.

/ 9

18. To my brother's annoyance, the child friendly rollercoaster is closed for repairs.

Apostrophes

> Underline either **it's** or **its** to complete each sentence. For example:
>
> **(It's Its)** about time that I tidied my messy bedroom.

1. I saw a bird making **(it's its)** nest in a tree in our back garden.

2. **(It's Its)** my dream to become the best ice skater in my school.

3. Dad is taking us to the seaside even though **(it's its)** far away.

4. Ted had to repair his guitar because **(it's its)** strings had snapped.

5. Even when **(it's its)** not Max's fault, he always gets the blame.

6. Until the storm stopped raging, the bear didn't leave **(it's its)** den.

7. Priya thinks **(it's its)** hilarious to sneak up on me and make me jump.

8. Sarah tried turning on her computer, but **(it's its)** screen was broken.

9. Although **(it's its)** challenging, snowboarding is an incredibly fun sport.

/ 9

> One word in each sentence is missing an apostrophe. Underline the word and write the correct version on the line. For example:
>
> We <u>cant</u> carry that heavy box. _____can't_____

10. Lillys siblings always win medals at running competitions. _____

11. The restaurant isnt serving lunch until later in the day. _____

12. Chris and Heidi said theyve been on the Ferris wheel. _____

13. The butterflies wings were delicate and multicoloured. _____

14. Mariko hasnt finished the novel that she is reading. _____

15. Saskia said the missing mittens were yours, not Jacobs. _____

16. The childrens paintings were displayed in their classrooms. _____

17. You mustnt touch any of the artefacts in the cabinets. _____

/ 9

18. The cows bells jangled as they plodded around the field. _____

Inverted Commas, Colons and Semicolons

Inverted Commas

Rewrite the reported speech as direct speech. For example:

> Mum announced that she is having a baby.
> "I'm having a baby," Mum announced.

1. Beth said that Din found a caterpillar.

    _____

2. We asked what time it is.

    _____

3. Diego exclaimed that he won the lottery.

    _____

4. She speculated that it might snow later.

    _____

5. Haru advised me to keep a diary.

    _____

/ 5

Colons & Semicolons

Add a colon or a semicolon to complete each sentence. For example:

> I couldn't believe what my dad built: a giant tree house.

6. Put these things in your backpack a book, some pencils and your lunch box.

7. Zoey grinned when she saw her best friend they had been apart for too long.

8. Marcus had just one mission in life to find the world's tastiest chocolate biscuits.

9. Isabelle has three pets a fluffy puppy, an excitable hamster and a timid cat.

10. The actors worked extremely hard the performance was a huge success.

11. I love visiting my dad's old farm the lake near my school; and Aunt Jane's house.

12. Julius breathed a sigh of relief no one had seen him escape.

13. There was only one way that Ron wanted to travel by using a zipwire.

14. Fatima sprinted to the window another shooting star whizzed past.

/ 9

Mixed Punctuation Questions

Each of these sentences is missing one punctuation mark. Add the missing punctuation mark to each of the sentences. For example:

> The farmer was rebuilding the ponies' stable .

1. " Would you like to go sledging with me " asked Dylan .

2. Timo pushed the snowball which was rather large , down the steep hill .

3. " Please can I borrow the purple paint ? Amahle asked Freddy .

4. There were expensive items in the box a gold ring , diamonds and a necklace .

5. An ancient coin lost for a thousand years , has finally been unearthed .

6. The ladies table was reserved for ten o'clock in the morning .

7. Clara's house (built in 1920 has a secret underground passageway .

8. " Make sure you take lots of pictures " Dad advised me .

9. In the summer , sweet smelling flowers bloom in my garden .

/ 9

There are **two** punctuation mistakes in each of the following sentences. Write out each sentence correctly. For example:

> Macys tired out brother went to bed.
>
> <u>Macy's tired-out brother went to bed.</u>

10. Its nearly time to drive to scotland.

_____

11. "I cant believe that happened," Laughed Reece.

_____

12. You need these items, glue paper and glitter.

_____

13. Helen a world famous author — lives there.

/ 8

_____

Mixed Punctuation Questions

These passages have no punctuation. Rewrite the passages with the correct punctuation. Each passage has 10 missing punctuation marks.

1. we have got to find the last item and win the scavenger hunt said bobby his team had found three things on the list some chalk a tennis ball and a book about insects

_____

_____

_____

_____

/ 10

_____

2. like whippets they scampered into the forest gradually bobbys short lived confidence turned into mild despair when he realised his teams chances were low

_____

_____

_____

_____

/ 10

_____

3. has anyone seen any sign of a pink flower yet bobby asked in an urgent voice his team dirty from searching through piles of mud and leaves shook their heads

_____

_____

_____

_____

/ 10

_____

Plurals

Plurals

Write the correct plural of the word in brackets. For example:

> She has three cats and two __canaries__ (canary).

1. We visited four _____ (city) on our trip to Italy.

2. Hamza's cat definitely has nine _____ (life).

3. The _____ (chef) worked together to make a delicious meal.

4. Tansy and I picked some _____ (berry) to make a crumble.

5. I had four _____ (stitch) in my foot after I cut it on some glass.

6. My dad owns five _____ (radio) — he likes to have one in every room.

7. Kieran put up the _____ (shelf), but they were wonky.

8. Nat and I saw some _____ (flash) of lightning last night.

9. I enjoyed the walk, but I was bitten by several _____ (mosquito).

/ 9

Plurals

Write the correct plural of the word in brackets. For example:

> My brother has planted several __cacti__ (cactus) in a pot.

10. Two of my great-grandfathers were _____ (airman) during the war.

11. Looking across the field, I saw a flock of _____ (sheep) bounding towards me.

12. There were two _____ (moose) peering at Alika from behind the bushes.

13. They are making three more _____ (series) of my favourite TV show.

14. Do you want one of _____ (this) jumpers that I've made?

15. Amber asked ten _____ (person) to name their favourite book.

16. My grandparents live in one of _____ (that) houses over there.

17. Kian peered up at the flock of _____ (goose) soaring above.

18. The _____ (mouse) scurried frantically across the floor.

Hint: These plurals are irregular, so think carefully about each one.

/ 9

Homophones

Homophones

Choose the correct homophone from the brackets. For example:

> I want to ___be___ (**be** **bee**) in the school play.

1. Katy resisted the temptation to _____ (**peek** **peak**) at her birthday present.

2. My big sister bought some bright red hair _____ (**die** **dye**).

3. The little wooden boat was moored to a blue _____ (**boy** **buoy**).

4. My dad _____ (**ode** **owed**) me two pounds for mowing the lawn.

5. I made a decoration from an old cotton _____ (**reel** **real**) and some felt.

6. Giraffes have an unusual _____ (**gate** **gait**) because their legs are so long.

7. The puppy started to _____ (**nor** **gnaw**) on the toy we bought him.

8. For my stepmum's birthday, we visited a luxury _____ (**spa** **spar**).

9. We went windsurfing on a _____ (**lock** **loch**) during our holiday.

/ 9

Homophones

Underline the correct homophone to complete the sentence. For example:

> Paolo decided to (**where** **wear** **ware**) his new shirt.

10. Adeel planned to (**so** **sew** **sow**) some tomato seeds in the garden.

11. Laurie tried to (**sees** **seas** **seize**) the remote control, but I grabbed it first.

12. I didn't rush to meet my friends because (**there** **their** **they're**) always late.

13. Jenny and Joe saw a (**pear** **pair** **pare**) of kingfishers by the river.

14. My grandad likes to talk about the olden days — he calls them 'days of (**your** **you're** **yore**)'.

15. My brother is really (**vain** **vein** **vane**) and spends hours in front of the mirror.

16. Normally, I lay the table and my sister (**paws** **pours** **pause**) the water for dinner.

17. I ran really fast because I wanted to (**raise** **rays** **raze**) my heart rate.

18. The issue of climate change has come to the (**for** **fore** **four**) in recent years.

/ 9

Prefixes and Suffixes

Prefixes

Choose the correct prefix from the list to complete the word in each sentence: **un**, **in**, **pre**, **mis**, **re** or **dis**. For example:

> I didn't know how to _re_ act when the magician pointed at me.

1. The curry has an ____tense and aromatic flavour.

2. Dinosaurs ____date the existence of humans by millions of years.

3. We had an ____eventful evening at Grandma's house.

4. The Coopers had to ____arrange the delivery date because it clashed with their holiday.

5. Poor Mr Devi ____heard the instruction and went through the bog instead of round it.

6. I thought Sally would look like her sister, but they were quite ____similar.

7. Mum always tells me to read the questions properly to avoid making ____takes.

8. Harrison's footwear was completely ____adequate for climbing a mountain.

9. Gudrun competed in the race to try and ____gain the title.

/ 9

Suffixes

Complete these sentences by adding a suffix to the word in brackets. For example:

> We all cheered as the final _runner_ (**run**) crossed the finish line.

10. The quality of her performance left me _____ (**speech**).

11. Bhavna was amazed by the dancer's precise _____ (**move**).

12. Tommy couldn't help but feel that the accident was _____ (**prevent**).

13. We were excited to receive the _____ (**invite**) to the party.

14. I was quite surprised by the _____ (**heavy**) of the bags.

15. Amy started a _____ (**malice**) rumour about what had happened.

16. In the end, Simon's _____ (**persist**) paid off and he finished the puzzle.

17. Carla got in trouble for speaking _____ (**cheeky**) to Mrs Ray.

/ 9

18. Jaden was very _____ (**compliment**) about the painting.

Awkward Spellings

Vowels

Underline the correct spelling of the word in brackets to complete the sentence. For example:

We planned a party for my uncle's (**fiftieth**   **fifteith**) birthday.

1. The (**pateint**   **patient**) in the bed next to me had a broken leg.

2. The architect (**unveiled**   **unvieled**) her plans for the new recreation centre.

3. I always make sure I (**weigh**   **wiegh**) my ingredients accurately before baking.

4. Jennet wasn't usually (**decietful**   **deceitful**), so I was surprised by her lie.

5. Jay completed his chores with maximum (**efficiency**   **efficeincy**) so he could go out.

6. We tried our best in the test to (**achieve**   **acheive**) a good mark.

7. Martha couldn't (**concieve**   **conceive**) of a more pleasant way to spend the day.

8. I lost the (**receipt**   **reciept**) for my laptop, so I couldn't return it.

9. My sister had a long list of (**grievances**   **greivances**) about her last job.

/ 9

Consonants

Complete these words with the correct pair of consonants so that the sentence makes sense. For example:

Emma couldn't believe her new o_ff_ice was in a ca_st_le.

10. Hardi came up with a s____eme to increase le____uce production on the allotment.

11. I ha____en to have hurt my ____uckle, so I can't hold a pen.

12. The word had too many sy____ables, so it ruined the ____ythm of my poem.

13. Jaz was a____ointed as the group leader for their climb to the su____it.

14. Pia ____inkled her nose when she saw how po____uted the water was.

15. They said the lemon tart was bi____er, but they only left cru____s on the plate.

16. That year, William had a____anged to visit three forei____ countries on holiday.

17. It was always a ____ench leaving the farm, but this time felt di____erent.

18. Olly had an o____asional ache in his arm, but mostly it felt nu____.

> Hint: Each space needs either a pair of double letters or has one silent letter.

/ 9

Section Three — Spelling

Mixed Spelling Questions

Underline the correct word to complete each sentence. For example:

Bex stood by her (**principle** **principal**) of not working Sundays.

1. Mum announced that she wanted to (**lie** **lay**) down for an hour.

2. I asked Sadiq to (**lie** **lay**) the ornament down gently.

3. The overall (**affect** **effect**) of the music was beautiful.

4. My group studied how temperature can (**affect** **effect**) plant growth.

5. My brother Saul had to (**ensure** **insure**) his car before he could drive it.

6. I always (**ensure** **insure**) I have a bowl of popcorn ready before the film starts.

7. We had to dress (**formally** **formerly**) for my cousin's wedding.

8. Much of Britain was (**formally** **formerly**) covered in ice.

9. I saw a new (**addition** **edition**) of my favourite book in the shop.

/ 10

10. The (**addition** **edition**) of chilli made the soup much tastier.

Each sentence contains a spelling mistake. Underline the word with the error and write the correct spelling on the line. For example:

I checked the <u>calender</u> to see if I was free. _calendar_

11. Kim told a humourous anecdote that made everyone chuckle. _____

12. It soon became apparant that the guide didn't know the route. _____

13. It was an extremely special ocasion, so I wore my finest outfit. _____

14. Li saw some massive llamas and minature cows in the pasture. _____

15. I felt greatful for the opportunity to interview my favourite artist. _____

16. We weren't informed that we required a lisence to sail here. _____

17. Steve damaged the precious vase, but it occurred accidentaly. _____

18. Diving was a marvellous experiance; I'll definitely go again. _____

/ 8

Alliteration and Onomatopoeia

Alliteration

Underline all the words that form the alliteration. For example:

Susie slyly snuck all of the sweets into her satchel.

1. The mouse marvelled at the massive mountain made of cheese.

2. Herbert honestly had no idea how to help with Harriet's homework.

3. Kathy couldn't count the considerable number of kangaroos.

4. Walter wrapped Wilma's presents while she was out.

5. Surprisingly, this sweet perfume has not been sold for a century.

6. At the party, plenty of people got their photograph taken by Polly.

7. The chef let out a shriek when Charlotte dropped the plate of shrimp.

8. In June, Julia said she was going to the jungle to search for gemstones.

9. If I'd known there would be gnats, I would never have gone near the swamp.

Hint: Look for words that have the same sound at the beginning, not just the same letter.

/ 9

Onomatopoeia

Underline the onomatopoeic word from the brackets to complete each sentence. For example:

The teacher **(quietened hushed calmed)** the pupils.

10. The baby **(laughed gurgled smiled)** happily when I picked her up.

11. Water was **(gushing pouring flooding)** out of the drainpipe during the storm.

12. From our cabin, we could hear wolves **(crying fighting howling)** in the distance.

13. I was lying in my garden when a butterfly **(flew fluttered circled)** over my head.

14. The heavy bowling ball **(dropped landed thudded)** loudly on the floor.

15. At the start of a meal, people sometimes **(clink hit touch)** their glasses together.

16. Umar could hear his pot of soup **(moving rolling sloshing)** around in his bag.

17. Dario could hear raindrops **(falling streaming pattering)** onto his umbrella.

18. Izara **(talks murmurs shouts)** in her sleep when she is having a bad dream.

/ 9

Imagery

Imagery

Each sentence contains a metaphor, simile or personification. Write down which technique is being used for each sentence. For example:

Thiago's eyes sparkled like stars. _____simile_____

1. The still lake is a mirror reflecting the surrounding hills. _____

2. The kettle wailed in protest as the water boiled. _____

3. Camila's irritable teacher is snappy like a crocodile. _____

4. My friend Amelie is a lighthouse on a stormy night. _____

5. Our dog is a vacuum cleaner and will eat anything. _____

6. Nora entered the kitchen as ravenous as a lion. _____

7. Lucas stroked the kitten as gently as waves lap the shore. _____

8. The clouds threatened to drench the village with rain. _____

9. The leaves on the trees danced gracefully in the wind. _____

/ 9

Imagery

Complete these similes and metaphors using a suitable word or phrase. For example:

The cave was _a gaping mouth._

10. The engine was as loud as _____.

11. The enormous mountain was a _____.

12. The river twisted along like a _____.

13. Her heavy bag was a _____.

14. Patrick looks as calm as _____.

15. The captivating song was a _____.

16. The temperature was hot like _____.

17. My athletic sister is a _____.

18. Rahim was as excited as _____.

/ 9

Abbreviations

Underline the abbreviation and then write it out in full. For example:

Sid joined the Friends of Ferrets <u>Assoc.</u>   _____Association_____

1. The weather is cold enough in Dec for it to snow.   _____

2. Jade collected her medicine from Dr Marshall yesterday.   _____

3. Jonathan accidentally bought 50 kg of potatoes.   _____

4. The min amount of money that you can spend is 5 pounds.   _____

5. Capt Campbell said the ship would set sail soon.   _____

6. My friend wants to book an appt to get her hair cut.   _____

7. On Tues, Myra is going to play netball after school.   _____

8. I cannot believe my baby brother is already 3 wks old.   _____

9. Niesha has been promoted to Head of Govt Security.   _____

/ 9

Write down whether the word in bold is an acronym or an abbreviated word. For example:

The **UN** deals with global problems.   _____acronym_____

10. Miss Farnham wants us to hand in our projects **ASAP**.   _____

11. **Pres** García studied law at university.   _____

12. My best friend's **DOB** is 17 July 2010.   _____

13. Freya's mum bought a new **DAB** radio in the sales.   _____

14. My sister is taking an English **Lang** course at college.   _____

15. Her mum does lots of **DIY** projects at home.   _____

16. When I went backpacking, my bag weighed 50 **lb**.   _____

17. My grandparents live at **No.** 23 Strawberry Lane.   _____

18. The celebrities were allowed into the **VIP** area.   _____

/ 9

Synonyms and Antonyms

Synonyms

Underline the word from the brackets that is the best synonym for the word in bold. For example:

I was **envious** when I saw Lara's shoes. (**jealous** **insecure** **resentful**)

1. My sister gets **irritated** when I imitate her. (**outraged** **irked** **surly**)

2. Dan is known for his **reckless** behaviour. (**brave** **irresponsible** **defiant**)

3. I **anticipated** that Gwen would be late. (**hoped** **predicted** **suggested**)

4. The question looked easy, but looks can be **deceptive**. (**fake** **puzzling** **misleading**)

5. The ballerina moved **elegantly** across the dance floor. (**gracefully** **carefully** **discreetly**)

6. My teacher encourages us to be **inquisitive**. (**thoughtful** **alert** **curious**)

7. Our neighbour's dog can be **aggressive**. (**loud** **angry** **hostile**)

8. Explorers had to **decipher** the ancient markings. (**uncover** **describe** **interpret**)

9. Alexei **noticed** that Joe was upset. (**acknowledged** **discovered** **perceived**)

Hint: Synonyms are words that have the same meaning.

/ 9

Antonyms

Underline the word from the brackets that is the best antonym for the word in bold. For example:

I felt **weary** after going running. (**energised** **active** **content**)

10. Their house was decorated with **modern** furniture. (**unpopular** **dated** **damaged**)

11. Playing in the mansion's attic was **forbidden**. (**recommended** **harmless** **permitted**)

12. Kylie was **hesitant** to go surfing at the weekend. (**eager** **inspired** **brave**)

13. Tao was **repulsed** by the slimy slug on his shoe. (**bemused** **surprised** **delighted**)

14. The time we had left in the pool was **extended**. (**shortened** **inhibited** **delayed**)

15. The library has an **immense** collection of books. (**standard** **minuscule** **delicate**)

16. The hotel was known for its **tranquil** atmosphere. (**intimidating** **chaotic** **unpleasant**)

17. The tennis player **angered** the umpire. (**fascinated** **impressed** **appeased**)

18. The bracelet is my most **treasured** possession. (**boring** **despised** **unattractive**)

/ 9

Spotting and Understanding Devices

Read the passage below, then answer the questions that follow.

Students swarmed into the school canteen, coins clutched in hands, ready for the annual bake sale. Amani smiled nervously as her classmates flocked like seagulls around her table, peering and pointing at the plates of brownies, cupcakes and flapjacks that she had made the night before.

5   "This is so cool!" Amani's friend Josh exclaimed, handing over 20 p in exchange for a cupcake decorated like an alien. The cake grinned up at him as he chomped down on it.

As word about Amani's stash of sweet treats spread, the sea of faces, bobbing up to catch a glimpse of what she had to offer, became a rolling ocean.

10   Amani gulped, noticing that her table was looking barer by the second. Before the chattering crowd turned into a hungry mob demanding more delicious delicacies, she reached for reserves from a bag at her feet, refilling the plates as fast as they had been emptied.

Write down which technique is used in the following:

1. "flocked like seagulls" (line 2)   _____

2. "20 p" (line 5)   _____

3. "The cake grinned up at him" (lines 6-7)   _____

4. "as he chomped down on it" (line 7)   _____

5. "demanding more delicious delicacies" (line 11)   _____

/ 5

Underline the correct option for each question.

6. The author compares the crowd to "a rolling ocean" (line 9).
   This suggests that the crowd is:

   A moving.   B angry.   C shouting.

7. The author says that Amani "gulped" (line 10).
   What does this suggest about Amani?

   A She is terrified.   B She is nervous.   C She is hungry.

/ 2

Section Four — Writers' Techniques

Spotting and Understanding Devices

Read the passage below, then answer the questions that follow.

The wooden chest had waited patiently in the cellar for centuries, hoping a pair of inquisitive hands would reveal its contents with a click of its clasp and a heave of its lid. Though faces frequently appeared at the top of the cellar's stairs, few made it as far as the foot, preferring to peer into the gloom from above rather than brave the steps that groaned
5 ominously under their feet. Those who had dared to delve deeper soon grew disheartened, the boxes they opened only coughing up dust as opposed to secrets. Eventually, the people would leave, and the chest remained closed in a room as silent as a graveyard.

Until, that is, the day a small silhouette appeared in the doorway. After taking the first
10 step warily, a bird alighting on a branch, the child charged down with a careless clatter, clambering over the first few rows of boxes to reach those unopened. Catching a glimpse of golden light gleaming from between the wooden slats of the chest buried in the corner, the child paused, overcome by a peculiar sensation that this prospect was one full of promise.

Write down an example from the text of each of the following:

1. a simile _____

2. a metaphor _____

3. personification _____

4. a synonym of 'timidly' _____

5. an antonym of 'ordinary' _____   / 5

Underline the correct option for each question.

6. The author says that the chest's lid would open with a "heave" (line 2).
   What does this suggest about the chest?

   A It is very old.   **B** It is difficult to open.   **C** It is full of objects.

7. The stairs groaned "ominously" (line 5) when people walked down them.
   What effect does this word have?

   / 2

   A It shows the steps' age.   **B** The cellar seems louder.   **C** It creates tension.

Writing Fiction

Clauses

Add a clause in each gap to complete the sentences. Make sure your writing is exciting and interesting. For example:

Kie ran downstairs, _nearly tripping in his haste to get away._

1. Saffy raised her hand _____

2. _____ Ali sauntered down the road.

3. _____ the girl looked up.

4. He picked up the pen _____

5. Zaki shook his head _____

6. _____ Helena laughed out loud.

7. The crowd drifted away _____

8. Miles cheered loudly _____

9. _____ he pulled on the rope.

/ 9

Adjectives

You can improve your writing by using a variety of adjectives. Add adjectives to each sentence to make it more interesting. For example:

The _indignant_ chicken squawked and flapped its __heavy__ wings.

10. We ran along the _____ path and through the _____ wood.

11. My _____ sister came out dressed in her _____ coat.

12. Kaya plucked the _____ apple from the _____ tree.

13. The _____ donkey wandered around the _____ field.

14. Pip gave a _____ sigh and closed the _____ book.

15. Whistling a _____ tune, the _____ man strode down the road.

16. Hattie walked past the _____ house and into the _____ tunnel.

17. The _____ meadow was alive with the _____ hum of insects.

18. I trudged up the _____ stairs and along the _____ corridor.

/ 9

Writing Fiction

Section Five — Writing

Adjectives

Adjectives make your stories more detailed and interesting. Write two adjectives to describe each character or setting, then use your adjectives to write a sentence describing that character or setting. For example:

A wood ___lush___ ___cool___
The lush leaves cast cool shadows on the forest floor.

1. A library _____ _____

/ 2

2. A nurse _____ _____

/ 2

3. A school hall _____ _____

/ 2

4. A beach _____ _____

/ 2

5. A diver _____ _____

/ 2

6. A dog _____ _____

/ 2

Write a plan for each of these titles, then turn your plan into a story.
Try to write about 500 words for each.

7. Write a story with the title "An Unexpected Visitor".

8. Write a story with the title "Facing My Fears".

9. Write a story with the title "Beyond the Stars".

10. Write a story with the title "Hide and Seek".

Hint: Use the title as a starting point, but remember to be original — write about an unusual character or situation that will keep the reader interested.

11. Write a story that starts with the sentence "I peered blearily out at the sun pushing its way slowly upward, burning a thin mist from the lawn; it was the perfect day for an adventure."

Writing Non-Fiction

You can improve your own writing by understanding the purpose of different texts. Write down whether each sentence is describing (D), persuading (P) or informing (I). For example:

Why wouldn't you want to get fitter, stronger and healthier? __P__

1. The gentle breeze carried the scent of heather from the distant moor. ____

2. Badgers' main food sources are insects, earthworms, grubs and eggs. ____

3. The small boy wailed miserably as the scarlet balloon floated upward. ____

4. Join us on our march and help make Podley a cleaner, safer place. ____

5. Fizz can be added to soft drinks by a process called carbonation. ____

6. It's clear that cats are superior to dogs — they're smarter and more fun. ____

7. Without the planet's atmosphere, life on Earth wouldn't exist. ____

/ 7

Write a plan for these essays. Include a point for the introduction, three points for the middle and a point for your conclusion. All three of your main points should be in favour of one side of the argument.

8. **Teachers should wear a uniform at school. Do you agree?**

Introduction: _____

Point 1: _____

Point 2: _____

Point 3: _____

Conclusion: _____

/ 5

9. **Should children aged 10 and over have the right to vote?**

Introduction: _____

Point 1: _____

Point 2: _____

Point 3: _____

Conclusion: _____

/ 5

Writing Non-Fiction

> Write a sentence arguing **for** and **against** each of these statements.
> For example:
>
> > **Shops shouldn't be allowed to give out plastic carrier bags.**
> >
> > **For:** Plastic carrier bags cause a lot of extra waste.
> >
> > **Against:** Plastic is stronger than materials like paper.

1. **It's better to play one sport than lots of sports.**

   For: _____

   Against: _____   / 2

2. **Children should have to help with housework.**

   For: _____

   Against: _____   / 2

3. **School holidays are too long.**

   For: _____

   Against: _____   / 2

4. **Children's access to social media should be limited.**

   For: _____

   Against: _____   / 2

5. **Secondary school students should be allowed to study only subjects they like.**

   For: _____

   Against: _____   / 2

> Write a plan for each of these titles, then turn your plan into a
> full answer. Try to write about 500 words for each.

6. Write an essay about what you would like to achieve in your lifetime.

7. Write a letter to the council persuading them to build a sports centre in your area.

8. Write an article for a club newsletter, informing readers about a recent victory for the club.

9. Children should spend time outside every day. Do you agree?

10. Write an essay about your favourite time of year.

Assessment Test 1

The rest of this book contains six assessment tests, which get progressively harder.
Allow 50 minutes to do each test and work as quickly and as carefully as you can.

If you want to attempt each test more than once, you will need to print
multiple-choice answer sheets for these questions from our website
— go to cgpbooks.co.uk/11plus/answer-sheets or scan the QR code on the right.
If you'd prefer to answer the questions on the page, just follow the instructions in the question.

Answer
Sheets

> Read this passage carefully and answer the questions that follow.

An extract from 'Hag Storm'

"Ach, Rab, you're no fun anymore," Gil grumbled. "It's no that bad here, is it?"

Rab's only reply was to toss another stone into his basket so hard that it bounced out again.
He sighed wearily and stretched, trying to iron out all the kinks that had turned his back into a
scrunched-up accordion. Gil already knew the answer to that question anyhow. They both missed
5   their old life in the cottage at Alloway, with the school across the road and their friends living nearby,
ready for a game of soldiers after lessons. Here, life was a fight for survival like nothing Rab had ever
known.

Mount Oliphant looked pretty enough in October, Rab could admit that at least. The sun shone
gold on the newly harvested fields, and a flock of wild geese looked like tiny sailboats swimming
10 across the endless blue of the sky. It seemed like the heavens were smiling down on the farm they'd
moved to. But Rab knew the prettiness was all just a trick of the light, hiding the rotten truth beneath.

The land was so poor it was sucking the life from them and their father as they toiled over it, and
in the winter their hilltop farm did little to keep the cold and damp from the family huddled inside.
Even the princely sum of the hundred pounds their father had borrowed from their landlord hadn't
15 been enough to keep up with repairs, and now they had heavy debt to add to their struggles.

"It's a rare sight, though, is it no?" Gil tried again, nudging Rab and trying to coax a smile
from him.

"Aye, it's no bad," Rab had to admit.

The one thing their farm had going for it was the view. Looking west in the full glow of autumn
20 was enough to lift Rab's spirits no matter how tired he was.

by Victoria Williamson

> Answer these questions about the text that you've just read.
> Circle the letter of the correct answer.

1. Which word best describes how Gil feels at the start of the extract?

   A Nervous
   B Angry
   C Uninterested
   D Annoyed
   E Bored

   / 1

Carry on to the next question → →

2. Which of the following is not mentioned in the text?

   A The name of the place where Rab and Gil live now.
   B The amount of money Rab and Gil's father borrowed.
   C The type of crop grown on the farm.
   D The name of the place where Rab and Gil previously lived.
   E The activity that Rab is doing on the farm.

3. What is Gil trying to do in lines 16-17?

   A Annoy Rab
   B Cheer Rab up
   C Upset Rab
   D Make Rab laugh
   E Tease Rab

4. Which of the following does Rab miss about where they used to live?

   A The view from their cottage.
   B The golden fields.
   C The school being on the next road.
   D The games that he played with friends.
   E The lessons given by their favourite teacher.

5. Which of the following statements is true?

   A Gil doesn't miss where they used to live.
   B Rab finds the work on the farm easy.
   C The extract takes place in the winter.
   D The farm is exposed to harsh weather conditions.
   E Rab doesn't like anything about where they currently live.

6. Which of the following facts is given in the text?

   A Who Rab and Gil's father owes money to.
   B How long Rab and Gil have lived in their current house.
   C How far away Rab and Gil's old house is.
   D How many people are in their family.
   E Why Rab and Gil moved house.

7. Which of the following is not mentioned as a reason why life is a "fight for survival" (line 6)?

   A The house is in poor repair.
   B The land is difficult to farm.
   C They are struggling with money.
   D The weather is severe in winter.
   E They don't have enough food to eat.

8. How do you think Rab feels at the end of the passage?

   A Appreciative
   B Negative
   C Excited
   D Frustrated
   E Distressed

/ 7

Answer these questions about the way words and phrases are used in the passage.

9. Which of these is closest in meaning to "huddled" (line 13)?

   A Sheltered
   B Silently hidden
   C Assembled neatly
   D Locked
   E Grouped together

10. Which of these words is closest in meaning to "admit" (line 8)?

   A Consider
   B Believe
   C Accept
   D Understand
   E Notice

11. The word "toiled" (line 12) could most accurately be replaced by:

   A laboured.
   B cried.
   C worried.
   D trudged.
   E fought.

12. What type of word is "wearily" (line 3)?

   A Preposition
   B Verb
   C Adjective
   D Adverb
   E Conjunction

13. "a flock of wild geese looked like tiny sailboats swimming" (line 9).
    This is an example of:

   A an exclamation.
   B a metaphor.
   C a cliché.
   D onomatopoeia.
   E a simile.

14. "It seemed like the heavens were smiling down on the farm" (line 10).
    What is this sentence an example of?

   A A proverb
   B Personification
   C A pun
   D Alliteration
   E A rhyme

/ 6

Carry on to the next question → →

Read this passage carefully and answer the questions that follow.

The Festival of Colours

Holi, otherwise known as the Festival of Colours, is a religious celebration that originated in India. Records show that this festival has been celebrated by those of the Hindu faith for at least 1600 years, since the 4th century. Over the centuries, knowledge of the festival has been conveyed around the globe, and it is observed in many countries by Hindus and non-Hindus alike.

5   Although there is speculation about why Holi began, many believe that the story of Prahlad and his father, alternatively known as the Demon King, inspired the festival. According to legend, the Demon King prohibited the worship of gods, as he considered himself as powerful as a god and demanded people treat him as one instead. In defiance of his cruel father, Prahlad continued to worship the Hindu god Vishnu. The Demon King retaliated by tricking Prahlad into joining Holika —
10 Prahlad's evil aunt who was immune to fire — on a wooden pyre, which was subsequently set alight. However, the flames failed to burn Prahlad, as he had prayed to Vishnu for protection, whilst Holika, who supported the Demon King, perished in the blaze. The story of Vishnu's victorious rescue of Prahlad is one of the reasons Hindus consider Holi to signify the triumph of good over evil.

The festival takes place over two days in springtime, the first of which is called Holika Dahan.
15 In the evening, people congregate around bonfires and perform sacred rituals to overcome any evil in their lives. The following day, Rangwali Holi, is a day of colourful chaos in which children and adults arm themselves with water guns and water balloons to drench those around them, before hurling multicoloured powders at one another until each person is a vibrant rainbow. Throughout the day, cities and towns rejoice to the sound of folk music and in the taste of traditional delicacies; by the end
20 of the annual celebration, people return to their homes weary but satisfied.

Answer these questions about the text that you've just read.
Circle the letter of the correct answer.

15. According to the passage, which statement about Holi is true?

    A   Holi isn't associated with a religion.
    B   Holi was first celebrated in 1600.
    C   Holi is celebrated by people who aren't Hindu.
    D   Holi is only celebrated in India.
    E   Holi is not a well-known festival.

16. Why did the Demon King try to stop people from worshipping the gods?

    A   He didn't believe in the existence of a higher power.
    B   He wanted people to worship him as a god instead.
    C   He didn't agree with certain aspects of the Hindu faith.
    D   He was worried that people would lose respect for him as their king.
    E   He thought it was unfair that gods were seen as better than humans.

/ 2

17. According to the text, why did Prahlad survive the fire?

   A He was protected from the flames by Vishnu.
   B Prahlad had always been immune to fire.
   C His faith in Vishnu gave him the strength to escape on his own.
   D Holika rebelled against the Demon King and saved Prahlad from the flames.
   E Other people who worshipped Vishnu rescued him from the blaze.

18. Why do you think the Demon King was willing to send Holika onto the pyre?

   A He thought she was responsible for Prahlad's behaviour.
   B He wanted to show Prahlad what would happen if he kept worshipping Vishnu.
   C He wanted to disgrace Holika so people didn't worship her instead.
   D He didn't think Holika would be in danger from the fire.
   E He hoped she would be able to convince Prahlad to stop worshipping Vishnu.

19. According to the passage, which statement about the legend of Prahlad is false?

   A The Demon King didn't approve of Vishnu.
   B Prahlad refused to listen to the Demon King.
   C Holika was related to Prahlad.
   D The Demon King set up a trap for Prahlad.
   E Holika survived the blaze and was cleansed of her evil nature.

20. Which of the following words best describes Rangwali Holi?

   A Destructive
   B Hilarious
   C Bewildering
   D Lively
   E Demanding

21. Which of the following is not mentioned in the text?

   A What Holi is alternatively known as.
   B How long Holi lasts.
   C Why people perform rituals at the bonfires.
   D How often Holi occurs.
   E The number of people who celebrate Holi.

22. According to the passage, what does Holi represent for Hindus?

   A A time for celebration with friends and family.
   B The defeat of evil by good.
   C A rebellion against the Demon King's wishes.
   D The proof that Hindus worship Vishnu.
   E A distraction from any problems in people's lives.

/ 6

Carry on to the next question → →

Answer these questions about the way words and phrases are used in the passage.

23. Which of these words is closest in meaning to "victorious" (line 12)?

   A Delighted
   B Capable
   C Fortunate
   D Encouraged
   E Successful

24. Which of these words is closest in meaning to "congregate" (line 15)?

   A Reunite
   B Swarm
   C Gather
   D Socialise
   E Approach

25. In the sentence "Holika, who supported the Demon King, perished in the blaze" (lines 11-12), which word is a preposition?

   A the
   B King
   C perished
   D in
   E blaze

26. What type of words are these?
evil   colourful   traditional

   A Proper nouns
   B Adjectives
   C Adverbs
   D Conjunctions
   E Verbs

27. "until each person is a vibrant rainbow." (line 18) What is this phrase an example of?

   A Onomatopoeia
   B Alliteration
   C A metaphor
   D Personification
   E A simile

28. "cities and towns rejoice to the sound of folk music" (line 19). Which technique is used here?

   A A cliché
   B Personification
   C A simile
   D Alliteration
   E Onomatopoeia

/ 6

In this passage, there are some spelling mistakes. Circle the letter which matches the part of the sentence with the mistake. If there's no mistake, circle N.

29. Sam hoped that the customers in his restaurant that evening had large apetites

      A   B   C   D   N

30. because he had discovered some extra potatoes in the seller. He planned to create

      A   B   C   D   N

31. a delicious shepherd's pie including the vegetable. As he prepared the evening meal,

      A   B   C   D   N

32. he thought about the flatterring compliments he was sure to receive. While the dish

      A   B   C   D   N

33. cooked, he glanced back to his special recipe for referance. He felt a sudden shock

      A   B   C   D   N

34. of anxeity when he saw he had added eight times the amount of potatoes he needed!

      A   B   C   D   N

/ 6

Choose the right word or phrase to complete this passage. Circle the letter which matches the correct word.

35. The departure board **on in under across to** the station clock flashed as the

          A B C   D   E

36. information updated. The travellers **have has was are had** been watching it closely.

             A   B   C   D   E

37. There was a groan **when what which who whether** they realised that the train

         A   B   C   D   E

38. had **be been being is done** cancelled. Jake took out his phone to call for a

   A   B   C   D E

39. taxi and realised **which when that then those** the battery had run out. Instead, he

        A   B   C   D   E

40. walked to the door with a **several few less more some** other people to catch a bus.

          A   B   C   D   E

/ 6

Carry on to the next question → →

Assessment Test 1

In this passage, there are some punctuation mistakes. Circle the letter which matches the part of the sentence with the mistake. If there's no mistake, circle N.

41. The village school is holding a fair on Sunday to raise money for some extra computers

| A | B | C | D | N |

42. As well as the usual raffle and tombola there will be a bouncy castle and some trampolines

| A | B | C | D | N |

43. on the sports field. People can help in several ways donating old clothes, baking

| A | B | C | D | N |

44. cakes and joining in on the day. Its not often that the whole community can come together

| A | B | C | D | N |

45. for such a good cause. The headteacher, Mrs Adams told the local paper that she hoped

| A | B | C | D | N |

46. many people would attend. "We are very excited to welcome all parents, children,

| A | B | C | D | N |

47. teachers and village residents to the fair," she said. I'm happy to see that there are

| A | B | C | D | N |

48. poster's up all over town to advertise the event. We hope it'll be a great success!" Last

| A | B | C | D | N |

49. year, the school raised enough money to replace their broken tennis equipment by

| A | B | C | D | N |

50. organising a weekly bake sale on Saturday afternoons throughout the Summer holidays.

| A | B | C | D | N |

/ 10

Total | / 50

End of Test

Assessment Test 2

Allow 50 minutes to do this test and work as quickly and as carefully as you can.

You can print **multiple-choice answer sheets** for these questions from our website —
go to cgpbooks.co.uk/11plus/answer-sheets or scan the QR code on the right. If you'd
prefer to answer the questions on the page, just follow the instructions in the question.

Answer
Sheets

Read this passage carefully and answer the questions that follow.

An extract from 'Esperanza Rising'

Papa had promised to meet her in the garden and he never disappointed her. She bent over to
pick a red bloom, fully opened, and pricked her finger on a vicious thorn. Big pearls of blood pulsed
from the tip of her thumb and she automatically thought, "bad luck." She quickly wrapped her hand in
the corner of her apron and dismissed the premonition. Then she cautiously clipped the blown rose
5   that had wounded her. Looking toward the horizon, she saw the last of the sun disappear behind the
Sierra Madre*. Darkness would settle quickly and a feeling of uneasiness and worry nagged at her.

Where was Papa? He had left early that morning with the *vaqueros** to work the cattle. And he was
always home before sundown, dusty from the mesquite* grasslands and stamping his feet on the patio
to get rid of the crusty dirt on his boots. Sometimes he even brought beef jerky that the cattlemen had
10 made, but Esperanza always had to find it first, searching his shirt pockets while he hugged her.

Tomorrow was her birthday and she knew that she would be serenaded at sunrise. Papa and the
men who lived on the ranch would congregate below her window, their rich, sweet voices singing
Las Mañanitas, the birthday song. She would run to her window and wave kisses to Papa and the
others, then downstairs she would open her gifts. She knew there would be a porcelain doll from Papa.
15 He had given her one every year since she was born. And Mama would give her something she had
made: linens, camisoles or blouses embroidered with her beautiful needlework. The linens always went
into the trunk at the end of her bed for *algún dia**, for someday.

| *Sierra Madre — *a mountain range* | *mesquite — *a thorny plant* | **by Pam Muñoz Ryan** |
| *vaqueros — *cattlemen* | *algún dia — *someday* | |

Answer these questions about the text that you've just read.
Circle the letter of the correct answer.

1. Which of the following words best describes Esperanza's father?

   A Spontaneous
   B Reliable
   C Carefree
   D Observant
   E Helpful

2. According to the text, why is Esperanza in the garden?

   A She is tending to the flowers.
   B She is waiting for her father.
   C She is picking flowers for her birthday.
   D She is looking after some of the cattle.
   E She is on her way to the grasslands for a walk.

/ 2

Carry on to the next question → →

3. Which of the following doesn't usually happen on Esperanza's birthday?

    A She is given a doll as a present.
    B People who live on the farm sing to her.
    C She receives a handmade gift from her mother.
    D Her father brings her beef jerky.
    E She watches her father from her window.

4. According to the text, why is Esperanza worried?

    A She thinks she won't get the birthday presents she wants.
    B She doesn't like being outside in the dark.
    C Her father is late in returning home.
    D It looks like there is going to be bad weather.
    E She thinks the cut on her finger might become infected.

5. Which of the following statements is false?

    A Esperanza has a superstitious reaction to cutting her finger.
    B There are mountains near Esperanza's house.
    C Esperanza cuts the flower that hurt her.
    D The flower that pricks Esperanza hasn't bloomed yet.
    E Esperanza wanted to pick a red flower.

6. Which of the following statements about Esperanza's father is false?

    A He usually works in an indoor environment.
    B He looks after animals as part of his job.
    C He tends to get home when it's light outside.
    D He has been out since the morning.
    E He occasionally brings home treats for Esperanza.

7. Which of the following statements about Esperanza is true?

    A Esperanza is slow to rise on the morning of her birthday.
    B Esperanza plans on keeping some of her birthday gifts for the future.
    C Esperanza and her father don't openly show affection.
    D Esperanza's bedroom is on the ground floor of her house.
    E Esperanza's mother isn't very good at sewing.

8. Which of the following is not mentioned in the text?

    A Where Esperanza puts some of the gifts from her mother.
    B What time of day her birthday celebrations begin.
    C The name of the song sung on Esperanza's birthday.
    D How many porcelain dolls Esperanza owns.
    E Whether Esperanza's father and the men of the ranch are good singers.

/ 6

Answer these questions about the way words and phrases are used in the passage.

9. Which of these words is closest in meaning to "nagged at" (line 6)?

   A Confused
   B Bothered
   C Terrified
   D Overcame
   E Startled

10. Which of these words is closest in meaning to "dismissed" (line 4)?

   A Overlooked
   B Considered
   C Discharged
   D Rejected
   E Disobeyed

11. What is meant by the word "premonition" (line 4)?

   A Advice
   B Significance
   C Feeling
   D Purpose
   E Inclination

12. What is meant by the word "embroidered" (line 16)?

   A Decorated
   B Created
   C Completed
   D Improved
   E Personalised

13. In the line "The linens always went into the trunk" (lines 16-17), which word is a preposition?

   A linens
   B always
   C went
   D into
   E the

14. What type of word is "automatically" (line 3)?

   A Common noun
   B Verb
   C Adjective
   D Conjunction
   E Adverb

/ 6

Carry on to the next question → →

Read this passage carefully and answer the questions that follow.

Alfie's Adventures

Holly frowned as she stroked Alfie, her petite tabby cat. Once again, he had returned from his nocturnal wanderings covered in a peculiar combination of mud, twigs and unidentifiable smudges, and was now settling down for a day of luxurious cat naps.

Holly had always been intrigued by where Alfie ventured to at night. One day, her curiosity
5   got the better of her and she concocted a plan: her brother's prize possession was a compact green camera which he attached to his helmet when skateboarding. When he was out one evening, she crept into his room to retrieve it and secured it to Alfie's collar. After waiting a couple of nights in vain for him to leave, Holly felt a tingle of excitement when she heard the thump of the cat flap as she lay in bed.

10   In the morning, Holly awoke to thoughts of what the footage might show. She imagined Alfie stalking through a jungle of twisted branches and prickly hedgerows, an intrepid explorer charting unknown lands. She felt sure she'd see him racing after all manner of panicked rodents, and maybe even challenging the neighbour's huge ginger tomcat to a fight.

With trembling hands, Holly recovered the camera and connected it to her computer. The
15   screen was crowded with images as Alfie pushed his way out of the cat flap into the dusky night. She saw him stop to survey his surroundings before skirting the garden and squeezing under the wooden fence behind the flowerbeds. He sped across their neighbours' manicured lawns, then approached a brightly lit building, which Holly recognised as the local 24-hour supermarket. He swerved past the automatic front door and trotted past a lonely delivery van parked by the trolleys. Down the far side
20   of the building, next to a door that was ajar, a group of supermarket workers were sitting at a picnic bench eating sandwiches. They greeted Alfie warmly with scratches under his chin — his favourite spot — and a tummy rub, which even Holly's parents weren't allowed to do. Over the next few hours, Alfie was fed delicious scraps of cheese and ham and spoiled with attention. *No wonder he goes there!* Holly thought with a chuckle.

Answer these questions about the text that you've just read.
Circle the letter of the correct answer.

15. Why do you think Holly frowns at the start of the passage?

   A   She is angry that Alfie has left mud on the floor.
   B   She is trying to guess where Alfie goes at night.
   C   She is working out how to borrow her brother's camera.
   D   She is frustrated that Alfie doesn't want to play.
   E   She is upset that Alfie has been fighting with the neighbour's cat.

16. Which word best describes Holly's brother's camera?

   A   Expensive
   B   Small
   C   Good quality
   D   Award-winning
   E   Well-protected

/ 2

17. Why do you think Holly feels excited when she hears the cat flap thud?

    A She is happy that Alfie is back home safely.
    B She thinks the camera footage could win her a prize.
    C She is finally going to find out where Alfie goes at night.
    D She is looking forward to a good night's sleep.
    E She is about to watch the footage from the camera.

18. Which word best describes what Holly thinks Alfie is like before she sees the footage?

    A Adventurous
    B Hostile
    C Hesitant
    D Intelligent
    E Spoilt

19. Which statement best describes the side door at the supermarket?

    A It is wide open.
    B It is unlocked, but closed.
    C It is broken.
    D It is slightly open.
    E It has blown open in the breeze.

20. Which of the following statements is true?

    A The supermarket only has one door.
    B There are several vans parked beside the trolleys.
    C The supermarket is next to Holly's house.
    D The supermarket workers know Alfie well.
    E The supermarket workers are eating a hot meal.

21. Which of the following statements is false?

    A Alfie enjoys being scratched under his chin.
    B Alfie runs through several gardens in the area.
    C The supermarket workers give Alfie their food.
    D Alfie enjoys sleeping during the day.
    E Alfie leaves the house every night.

22. According to the passage, which of the following statements is true?

    A The supermarket is open all night.
    B The supermarket is hard to see at night.
    C The supermarket workers are eating lunch inside the café.
    D The supermarket workers are selfish.
    E There are picnic benches behind the supermarket.

/ 6

Carry on to the next question → →

Answer these questions about the way words and phrases are used in the passage.

23. Which of these words is closest in meaning to the word "smudges" (line 2)?

    A Stripes
    B Spots
    C Scrapes
    D Scratches
    E Smears

24. Which of these words is closest in meaning to the word "luxurious" (line 3)?

    A Indulgent
    B Extended
    C Pleasant
    D Adequate
    E Essential

25. The word "skirting" (line 16) could most accurately be replaced by:

    A Going straight across
    B Going around the edge of
    C Leaving behind
    D Walking towards
    E Going halfway across

26. "When he was out one evening" (line 6)
Which of these words is a verb?

    A When
    B he
    C was
    D out
    E evening

27. What type of word is "twisted" (line 11)?

    A Verb
    B Abstract noun
    C Adverb
    D Adjective
    E Common noun

28. "she heard the thump of the cat flap" (line 8)
This is an example of:

    A Personification
    B Onomatopoeia
    C A metaphor
    D A cliché
    E An exclamation

/ 6

Choose the right word or phrase to complete this passage.
Circle the letter which matches the correct word.

29. Late at night, Isla peered **into by on among to** her garden, which was bathed
        A B C D E

30. in moonlight. Silent as a shadow, Isla slipped out to watch **past from within since in**
        A B C D E

31. her patio as the bushes began to **rustled rustles rustling rust rustle** .
        A B C D E

32. Her eyes widened when she **seen saw seeing sees see** five small shapes
        A B C D E

33. scurrying across the grass. When she saw what they **which was where what were** ,
        A B C D E

34. she smiled. It was a mother hedgehog and her children **go went going goes gone**
        A B C D E

exploring in the dark.

/ 6

In this passage, there are some punctuation mistakes. Circle the letter which
matches the part of the sentence with the mistake. If there's no mistake, circle N.

35. "Come and get your shoes on, everybody! Mum called. I hurried downstairs, the
   A   **B**   **C**   **D**   N

36. thought of going to (the aquarium (my favourite place ever) filling me with excitement.
   A   **B**   **C**   **D**   N

37. There were three creatures I couldn't wait to see an angelfish, an octopus and a
   A   **B**   **C**   **D**   N

38. hammerhead shark. I also love looking at schools of fish in the crystal-clear waters
   A   **B**   **C**   **D**   N

39. of the tanks, their scale's shimmering in the light. If I could live at the aquarium,
   A   **B**   **C**   **D**   N

40. I would — its definitely the most incredible place that I have ever visited.
   A   **B**   **C**   **D**   N

/ 6

Carry on to the next question → →

Assessment Test 2

In this passage, there are some spelling mistakes. Circle the letter which matches the part of the sentence with the mistake. If there's no mistake, circle N.

41. "I can't believe it!" exclaimed Nari, beaming joyusly at Liam. "Our band has secured its

    A   B   C   D   N

42. first gig! We're going to be famous — legendry, even!" The Crown Hotel, renowned

    A   B   C   D   N

43. for being the place where multitudes of bands had begun their careers, had invited Nari's

    A   B   C   D   N

44. group to perform next Saturday evening. In response, Liam's face went pail and he let out

    A   B   C   D   N

45. a wimper. "But we haven't perfected our new song yet, and the show is scheduled in two

    A   B   C   D   N

46. days!" The room fell silent as the band prosessed the complication. Their newest song

    A   B   C   D   N

47. had the potential to be their best, but without sufficiant practice, it could easily be

    A   B   C   D   N

48. their worst. "Well," Nari said, "we'll just have to put in extra effort. This is a remarkible

    A   B   C   D   N

49. oppurtunity for us and I refuse to let it go to waste. If we try hard and work together

    A   B   C   D   N

50. as a team, we can achieve anything," she ashured the band with a confident smile.

    A   B   C   D   N

/ 10

Total   / 50

End of Test

Assessment Test 3

Allow 50 minutes to do this test and work as quickly and as carefully as you can.

You can print **multiple-choice answer sheets** for these questions from our website —
go to cgpbooks.co.uk/11plus/answer-sheets or scan the QR code on the right. If you'd
prefer to answer the questions on the page, just follow the instructions in the question.

**Answer
Sheets**

> Read this passage carefully and answer the questions that follow.

The Great Outdoors

The scent of pine needles, the liquid trill of birdsong, the gentle caress of a warm breeze…
It seems to me there's nothing more pleasurable than spending time outdoors. Yet an increasing
number of us are forgoing the joys of nature in favour of TV, consoles and mobile phones; surveys
suggest that the average 5- to 16-year-old in the UK spends over 6 hours every day staring at a

5   screen. To add insult to injury, the amount of time young people spend in natural settings has
declined; on average, it's now only around a quarter of an hour each day.

There's no doubt that TV and the Internet can be informative and entertaining — nobody's
disputing that they have their place. But what about all that the natural world can teach us? Can
a video game really replicate the achievement of successfully navigating a route over treacherous

10   terrain? Can a TV documentary truly cultivate as profound an understanding of the natural world as
actually being there amongst forest or moor or mountain?

Options for enjoying the outdoors are vast and varied; from hiking or cycling to climbing trees or
wild swimming, there's truly an activity for everyone. Spending time in the natural world doesn't only
benefit the body; it's also good for the soul. Those who spend at least two hours a week immersed in

15   nature report higher levels of happiness and well-being than those who squander their free time inside.

So here's my plea: turn off your TV, cast aside your phone and get outside. Your destination could
be a local nature reserve, a rock-pool-peppered shore, a tree-lined park or your own back garden.
Wherever you end up, and however you opt to spend your time there, I guarantee you won't regret it.

> Answer these questions about the text that you've just read.
> Circle the letter of the correct answer.

1.   According to the passage, which of the following statements is false?

   A   The writer enjoys spending time in nature.
   B   The writer thinks that televisions serve no purpose.
   C   The writer thinks it is important to understand nature.
   D   The writer believes everyone should spend time outdoors.
   E   The writer believes people should spend less time looking at screens.

2.   Which of the following facts is not given in the passage?

   A   Whether the amount of time young people spend in natural settings has increased or decreased.
   B   How long young people spend looking at a screen each day.
   C   How long young people spend in natural settings each day.
   D   How long young people spend on their phones each day.
   E   How long people should spend outside each week to improve their well-being.

/ 2

Carry on to the next question → →

3. Which of the following activities is not mentioned in the text?

   A Mountain climbing
   B Walking
   C Outdoor swimming
   D Riding a bike
   E Tree-climbing

4. What does the writer suggest about navigating a route in the wilderness?

   A It is impossible to achieve.
   B It is more fun than playing a video game.
   C It is something to be proud of.
   D It takes years of training.
   E It is safe as long as you know what you are doing.

5. Which of these environments is not mentioned in the text?

   A Moorland
   B Highland
   C Woodland
   D Grassland
   E Coast

6. Why does the writer ask questions in the second paragraph?

   A They are confused about the benefits of nature.
   B They want to persuade readers to use the Internet for educational reasons.
   C They want to make readers think about the educational benefits of being outdoors.
   D They are not sure whether it is better to learn from TV or from the real world.
   E They want to emphasise how important it is to study nature at school.

7. How is spending time outdoors presented in this passage?

   A Thrilling but dangerous
   B Healthy and stimulating
   C Boring but informative
   D Fun and risk-free
   E Comforting and sleep-inducing

8. Which word best describes the writer's tone in this passage?

   A Balanced
   B Amusing
   C Neutral
   D Reassuring
   E Biased

   / 6

Answer these questions about the way words and phrases are used in the passage.

9. Which of the following phrases is closest in meaning to "To add insult to injury" (line 5)?

    A To cause harm to a person
    B To make matters worse
    C To seriously offend someone
    D To try to resolve a situation
    E To provoke an argument

10. Which of these phrases is closest in meaning to "forgoing" (line 3)?

    A Doing without
    B Giving in to
    C Not appreciating
    D Relishing in
    E Moving on from

11. The word "profound" (line 10) could most accurately be replaced by:

    A emotional.
    B intellectual.
    C sincere.
    D eager.
    E deep.

12. Which of these words is closest in meaning to "squander" (line 15)?

    A Destroy
    B Waste
    C Save
    D Spoil
    E Reduce

13. What technique is used in the phrase "gentle caress of a warm breeze" (line 1)?

    A A cliché
    B A metaphor
    C A simile
    D Personification
    E An allusion

14. What part of speech is "guarantee" (line 18)?

    A Adverb
    B Adjective
    C Noun
    D Verb
    E Pronoun

/ 6

Carry on to the next question → →

Assessment Test 3

> Read this poem carefully and answer the questions that follow.

An abridged version of 'Exiled'

Searching my heart for its true sorrow,
This is the thing I find to be:
That I am weary of words and people,
Sick of the city, wanting the sea;

5 Wanting the sticky, salty sweetness
Of the strong wind and shattered spray;
Wanting the loud sound and the soft sound
Of the big surf that breaks all day.

Always I climbed the wave at morning,
10 Shook the sand from my shoes at night,
That now am caught beneath great buildings
Stricken with noise, confused with light.

If I could hear the green piles* groaning
Under the windy wooden piers,
15 See once again the bobbing barrels,
And the black sticks that fence the weirs*,

If I could see the weedy mussels
Crusting the wrecked and rotting hulls*,
Hear once again the hungry crying
20 Overhead, of the wheeling gulls,

I should be happy, — that was happy
All day long on the coast of Maine*!
I have a need to hold and handle
Shells and anchors and ships again!

25 I should be happy, that am happy
Never at all since I came here.
I am too long away from water.
I have a need of water near.

by Edna St. Vincent Millay

*piles — *posts that act as supports*

*weirs — *barriers which control the flow of water*

*hulls — *the bodies of ships*

*Maine — *the northeasternmost US state*

> Answer these questions about the text that you've just read.
> Circle the letter of the correct answer.

15. Which adjective best describes the narrator's tone in the first two verses?

    A Frantic
    B Arrogant
    C Wistful
    D Embarrassed
    E Hopeful

16. In the first verse, what does the narrator dislike about the city?

    A The air pollution
    B How dirty it is
    C The lack of nature
    D How busy it is
    E How far away it is from the coast

/ 2

17. According to the poem, which statement about the sea is false?

    A The waves are large.
    B Barrels float on the water.
    C The sound it makes is always the same.
    D The waves crash throughout the day.
    E There is more than one pier.

18. According to the poem, how long did the narrator used to spend by the sea?

    A The whole day
    B Just the morning
    C All night
    D Just the afternoon
    E An hour every day

19. Which of the following best describes the ships in line 18?

    A Sheltered and disguised
    B Stranded and unreachable
    C Vandalised and derelict
    D Repaired and intact
    E Damaged and disintegrating

20. Which of these is not mentioned in the poem?

    A Boats
    B Rocks
    C Seabirds
    D Shellfish
    E Sea spray

21. Which of the following statements about the narrator is mostly likely to be true?

    A They are visiting the city briefly.
    B They have always lived in the city.
    C They are currently living in the city.
    D They have travelled to lots of cities.
    E They would like to live in the city.

22. Which of these statements best describes verse 7?

    A The narrator has always been unhappy in the city, but believes they would be happy by the sea.
    B The narrator used to be happy in the city, but now wants to move to the coast.
    C The narrator feels they don't deserve to be in happy in the city.
    D The narrator is unhappy in the city, but isn't sure what would make them happy.
    E The narrator feels they will be happy in the city if they stay there longer.

/ 6

Carry on to the next question → →

Answer these questions about the way words and phrases are used in the passage.

23. "sticky, salty sweetness" (line 5). This is an example of:

    A personification.
    B alliteration.
    C irony.
    D a simile.
    E a metaphor.

24. In the line, "And the black sticks that fence the weirs" (line 16), which word is a verb?

    A black
    B sticks
    C that
    D fence
    E weirs

25. Which of these is closest in meaning to the word "Stricken" (line 12)?

    A Discouraged
    B Severely damaged
    C Neglected
    D Deeply affected
    E Forcibly silenced

26. "green piles groaning" (line 13). This is an example of:

    A symbolism.
    B a proverb.
    C a rhetorical question.
    D repetition.
    E personification.

27. What does the word "wheeling" mean (line 20)?

    A Flying slowly
    B Intimidating
    C Flying in a circle
    D Shrieking
    E Swooping low

28. What type of word is "Maine" (line 22)?

    A Proper noun
    B Collective noun
    C Common noun
    D Pronoun
    E Plural

/ 6

In this passage, there are some punctuation mistakes. Circle the letter which matches the part of the sentence with the mistake. If there's no mistake, circle N.

29. Archery the use of a bow and arrow to hit a target, dates back centuries.

   A   B   C   D   N

30. Over the years, bows and arrows have been used to hunt wild animals as a

   A   B   C   D   N

31. weapon in battle; and to participate in target-practice competitions. One such

   A   B   C   D   N

32. competition is in the Olympics, where archers aim at targets around 70 metres-away.

   A   B   C   D   N

33. To hit the targets accurately, its important for these athletes to have steady hands.

   A   B   C   D   N

34. If their hands aren't steady, there's a chance the arrow will go wildly off course

   A   B   C   D   N

/ 6

In this passage, there are some spelling mistakes. Circle the letter which matches the part of the sentence with the mistake. If there's no mistake, circle N.

35. Visit Canine Kennel today and meet our newest dog, Sunshine, who is ready to be

   A   B   C   D   N

36. adopted. Sunshine is the friendliest and most faithfull companion anyone could ever

   A   B   C   D   N

37. wish for. She's peaceful in nature and not the least bit agressive. One of her most

   A   B   C   D   N

38. valuable qualitys is her ability to perceive when people are feeling miserable. She'll

   A   B   C   D   N

39. show you lots of affectian, which is guaranteed to elevate your mood. If you're

   A   B   C   D   N

40. doutting whether you'll ever find the perfect dog, we recommend meeting Sunshine.

   A   B   C   D   N

/ 6

Carry on to the next question → →

Assessment Test 3

Choose the right word or phrase to complete this passage.
Circle the letter which matches the correct word.

41. The mission was simple: gain access **in too out to as** the balcony by using a ladder,
    A   B   C   D   E

42. unpick the lock on the door, **sneaks sneaked snuck sneak sneaking**
    A   B   C   D   E

43. into the mansion and find the gemstone the thieves **has did done gone had** stolen.
    A   B   C   D   E

44. **Preparing Prepared Prepare Preparation Prepares** herself for the challenge,
    A   B   C   D   E

45. Elna took a deep breath, **soon while besides also nor** Dean got the ladder. Climbing
    A   B   C   D   E

46. up, Elna worried she **were made were making had made are made have made**
    A   B   C   D   E

47. a mistake **during from under than inside** the mission's planning stage. What if she
    A   B   C   D   E

48. had forgotten to take something into account? If they **did was were had have**
    A   B   C   D   E

49. caught, they would be in danger. **Past Despite Before Hence Except** her nerves got
    A   B   C   D   E

50. the better of her, she **focused focuses has focused focusing focus** her attention
    A   B   C   D   E

back on the ladder, deciding to take this mission one step at a time.

/ 10

End of Test

Assessment Test 4

Allow 50 minutes to do this test and work as quickly and as carefully as you can.

You can print **multiple-choice answer sheets** for these questions from our website — go to cgpbooks.co.uk/11plus/answer-sheets or scan the QR code on the right. If you'd prefer to answer the questions on the page, just follow the instructions in the question.

Answer Sheets

> Read this passage carefully and answer the questions that follow.

An extract from 'Out of Heart'

Thin slivers of light plunged through the square attic windows on Marrow Street. The small room in the Shah family house was a real suntrap and Adam would come here to think and draw, and to leave the shadows of the day behind. He lay down, staring up through the grimy glass at the blue rectangle of sky, and pulled out his battered, smudged notepad and a well-chewed pencil.

5   ***Suntrap. Sun trapped. Trapped son.***

Adam started sketching, trying to capture the sunlight in his drawing, but soon threw his pencil down in frustration. Then an image unfolded in his brain, a painting his art teacher, Mrs Matheson, had shown him. It was of Icarus, the boy who flew too close to the sun, and showed him lying on the rocks, the ground beneath strewn with feathers. He'd soared high, letting the winds carry him, to
10 show his father he wasn't scared. To show he could go higher. To show that he loved him. Adam understood then how you drew the sun — by showing broken wings on the rocks below. But Adam was more interested in Icarus *before* the fall. He seized his pencil and started drawing furiously. He drew Icarus, standing on the edge of the cliff looking down, wings unfurled, about to jump. Then he sketched the blurry shape of Icarus's father, Daedalus. As he traced Icarus's wings with his index
15 finger, Adam imagined Daedalus saying, *Don't fly too close to the sun or you'll perish. Promise me you won't fly too close to the sun?* In his mind's eye, he saw Icarus turning to say, *We have nothing to fear from the sun, Father. The sun gives us life.* Adam saw Icarus spread his wings and smile, and, with a last look at his father, jump.

by Irfan Master

> Answer these questions about the text that you've just read.
> Circle the letter of the correct answer.

1. Which of these words best describes the window in the attic room?

   A Dirty
   B Ornate
   C Rusty
   D Broken
   E Patterned

2. What do the "battered, smudged notepad" and "well-chewed pencil" (line 4) suggest about Adam?

   A He is generous with his possessions.
   B He isn't very well-behaved.
   C He is careful with his possessions.
   D He spends a lot of time drawing.
   E He isn't very good at drawing.

/ 2

Carry on to the next question → →

3. Why did Adam throw down his pencil?

   A He had broken it whilst sketching.
   B He couldn't draw because the sun was in his eyes.
   C He was struggling to draw the sunlight properly.
   D He had finished his drawing.
   E He was tired of drawing.

4. Which part of Icarus's story is Adam most interested in?

   A When he prepares to fly.
   B When he allows the wind to transport him.
   C When he falls to the ground.
   D When he reaches the sun.
   E When he flies higher to impress his father.

5. Which of the following statements about Adam's drawing of Icarus is false?

   A He draws Icarus on a cliff.
   B He draws a distinct picture of Daedalus.
   C He draws only two people in the picture.
   D He draws Icarus gazing downwards.
   E He draws a pair of wings.

6. In the conversation Adam imagines between Daedalus and Icarus, how do you think Daedalus feels when he asks Icarus not to "*fly too close to the sun*" (line 16)?

   A Vulnerable
   B Apprehensive
   C Timid
   D Content
   E Assured

7. Adam "started drawing furiously." (line 12) What does this phrase suggest?

   A He felt frustrated about drawing Icarus.
   B He felt inspired to draw Icarus.
   C He felt worried about drawing Icarus.
   D He felt angry about drawing Icarus.
   E He felt reluctant to draw Icarus.

8. How do you think Adam feels when he is in the attic room?

   A Appreciated and relaxed
   B Nervous and tense
   C Lonely and wistful
   D Safe and unburdened
   E Sombre and pensive

/ 6

Answer these questions about the way words and phrases are used in the passage.

9. Which word is closest in meaning to "plunged" (line 1)?

   A Ripped
   B Split
   C Flickered
   D Fell
   E Tripped

10. Which word could most accurately replace "unfurled" (line 13)?

   A Broad
   B Developed
   C Contracted
   D Open
   E Secured

11. Which of these is closest in meaning to "strewn" (line 9)?

   A Scattered
   B Concealed
   C Buried
   D Shattered
   E Camouflaged

12. "It was of Icarus, the boy who flew too close to the sun" (line 8).
    Which of these words is a pronoun?

   A Icarus
   B boy
   C who
   D close
   E sun

13. What type of words are "in" (line 2) and "beneath" (line 9)?

   A Nouns
   B Adverbs
   C Verbs
   D Conjunctions
   E Prepositions

14. "*The sun gives us life*" (line 17) is an example of:

   A an analogy.
   B a command.
   C a statement.
   D an exclamation.
   E an abbreviation.

/ 6

Carry on to the next question → →

Assessment Test 4

Read this passage carefully and answer the questions that follow.

How Coyote Stole Fire

Long ago, when mankind was new to Earth, there was joy and peace in abundance. In the springtime, flowers bloomed freely, opening their petals to greet the sun as humans looked on in wonder. In the summertime, the sun shone brightly, a steadfast source of strength and warmth. But each year, as winter crept closer, a fear as cold as ice chilled the humans' spines. Without the
5   sun's heat to alleviate the merciless cold, their lives would be at risk.

One day, Coyote overheard the humans' woes and whimpered. Other animals had furry coats and underground dens for shelter, both of which the humans lacked. Determined to be of assistance, Coyote went to the mountains in search of the Fire Spirits, who guarded the only fire in the land. However, the Fire Spirits were malicious beings, with vicious claws and eyes that burned like coals,
10 and Coyote knew they would not share their fire willingly.

When the Fire Spirits noticed Coyote lurking nearby, they thought him only a harmless, wolf-like creature, and paid him no mind. But Coyote studied their behaviour intently, waiting for a moment when the fire was left unprotected. Soon, the moment revealed itself: every morning, the Fire Spirit guard left to wake its replacement, leaving the crackling blaze briefly exposed. The following morning,
15 Coyote dashed to the fire and lowered a stick into it. Suddenly, a Fire Spirit emerged from its den with a snarl. At this, Coyote fled, the burning stick clenched in his jaws, the heat from the pursuing Fire Spirits singeing his fur. To protect the flame, Coyote hurled the stick onto a tree stump, which instantly closed around the fire to shield it. The Fire Spirits, who knew of no way to coax fire out of wood, soon returned to their camp. Free from danger, Coyote was able to trick the stump into
20 revealing how to extract the prized flames. He presented the fire to the humans, whose faces, at the sight of the precious heat source, lit up with hope.

Answer these questions about the text that you've just read.
Circle the letter of the correct answer.

15. According to the text, why are the humans scared of winter?

  A   They haven't experienced winter before.
  B   They don't have any way to keep warm.
  C   They worry that the Fire Spirits will steal their fire.
  D   They fear the dark and having less daylight.
  E   They worry that the land will be covered in ice.

16. How do you think Coyote felt when he overheard the humans worrying?

  A   Frustrated
  B   Guilty
  C   Concerned
  D   Angry
  E   Terrified

/ 2

17. Which of the following words best describes the Fire Spirits?

   A Deceitful
   B Judgemental
   C Bitter
   D Selfish
   E Manipulative

18. Which of the following statements about the humans in the story is false?

   A They delight in the natural world.
   B They haven't lived on Earth for long.
   C They rely on the sun for warmth.
   D They aren't as well-equipped as animals for the winter.
   E They are initially scared of Coyote.

19. According to the text, which statement about the Fire Spirits is true?

   A They live in an underground cave.
   B They only guard the fire at night.
   C They have a predictable routine.
   D They can create fire themselves.
   E They can't go near humans.

20. How did the Fire Spirits react when they first saw Coyote?

   A They were indifferent to him.
   B They were suspicious of him.
   C They were confused by him.
   D They thought he seemed pleasant.
   E They were afraid of him.

21. According to the text, why did the Fire Spirits eventually go back to their camp?

   A They couldn't catch up to Coyote.
   B They didn't know how to get the fire out of the tree.
   C They wanted to protect the fire that they had left.
   D They realised that the humans deserved the fire.
   E They thought the fire that Coyote stole had died out.

22. Which of the following is not mentioned in the text?

   A Which animal Coyote looks like
   B Why the fire is left unguarded
   C How far Coyote travels with the fire
   D When the fire is left unguarded
   E What Coyote uses to steal the fire

/ 6

Carry on to the next question → →

Answer these questions about the way words and phrases are used in the passage.

23. Which of these words is closest in meaning to "malicious" (line 9)?

   A Troublesome
   B Evil
   C Mischievous
   D Brutal
   E Unforgiving

24. What is meant by the word "abundance" (line 1)?

   A Uncountable amounts
   B Moderate supply
   C Decreasing amounts
   D Increasing amounts
   E Large supply

25. Which of these words is closest in meaning to "coax" (line 18)?

   A Force
   B Provoke
   C Command
   D Persuade
   E Pressure

26. In the line "But Coyote studied their behaviour intently" (line 12), which word is an adverb?

   A But
   B studied
   C their
   D behaviour
   E intently

27. "a steadfast source of strength and warmth." (line 3) What is this phrase an example of?

   A A metaphor
   B Personification
   C A simile
   D Alliteration
   E Onomatopoeia

28. "a fear as cold as ice chilled the humans' spines." (line 4) Which technique is used here?

   A A proverb
   B An abbreviation
   C A simile
   D Personification
   E Onomatopoeia

/ 6

In this passage, there are some spelling mistakes. Circle the letter which matches the part of the sentence with the mistake. If there's no mistake, circle N.

29. Although Talia was only two years old, she was fiercely independant. Constantly seeing

    A   B   C   D   N

30. her older brother, Bruno, successfully navigate the world without much assistence gave

    A   B   C   D   N

31. Talia the confidence to asert herself repeatedly, much to the frustration of her family.

    A   B   C   D   N

32. The minute they turned their backs on her, the girl clambered on furnature and attempted

    A   B   C   D   N

33. to use equipment intended for older children and adults. When it was Bruno's turn to

    A   B   C   D   N

34. look after Talia, he never had a moment's piece — every second with her was an adventure.

    A   B   C   D   N

/ 6

Choose the right word or phrase to complete this passage. Circle the letter which matches the correct word.

35. The caves **upon aside for near between** the village of Little Hollow are a popular

    A   B   C   D   E

36. tourist destination and are **visited visiting visits visitors visit** by thousands each

    A   B   C   D   E

37. year. The caves are **lights lit alight lighting lighter** by hundreds of small lanterns

    A   B   C   D   E

38. that guide people **despite during along by with** the underground tunnels.

    A   B   C   D   E

39. **Eventually Whereas Afterwards Additionally Although** , while people are

    A   B   C   D   E

40. exploring, they can **listened listen listener listens listening** to a recording about

    A   B   C   D   E

the caves' history.

/ 6

Carry on to the next question → →

Assessment Test 4

60

> In this passage, there are some punctuation mistakes. Circle the letter which matches the part of the sentence with the mistake. If there's no mistake, circle N.

41. The school play was five days away, and Declan couldn't remember a single one of his lines.

    A   B   C   D   N

42. No matter how much he read, spoke sang or even shouted them, the lines refused to

    A   B   C   D   N

43. remain in his head. "You need to find a way to relax, his teacher, Mr Ellison, told him.

    A   B   C   D   N

44. "Your brain is jam packed with nerves. Once you've calmed down, you'll have more space

    A   B   C   D   N

45. in your head for your lines." but Declan — seeing the hall filled with students setting up the

    A   B   C   D   N

46. stage only felt more anxious. Later that day, when his mum picked him up from school,

    A   B   C   D   N

47. he noticed that the hall was empty. "Mum, could I try something" Declan asked, walking

    A   B   C   D   N

48. timidly onto the stage. The room, which was now quiet and calm wasn't so intimidating.

    A   B   C   D   N

49. Suddenly, Declans lines came flooding back into his head, along with a plan. Today he would

    A   B   C   D   N

50. practise on the stage with his mum, tomorrow with his friends, and in five days hed be

    A   B   C   D   N

ready to face the school.

/ 10

Total   / 50

End of Test

Assessment Test 5

Allow 50 minutes to do this test and work as quickly and as carefully as you can.

You can print **multiple-choice answer sheets** for these questions from our website — go to cgpbooks.co.uk/11plus/answer-sheets or scan the QR code on the right. If you'd prefer to answer the questions on the page, just follow the instructions in the question.

Answer Sheets

Read this passage carefully and answer the questions that follow.

The Tunnels

Within minutes of entering the tunnels, Violet learned that no darkness is as terrifying as that holding the unknown. The gloom taunted them, once-harmless sounds becoming ominous. The scrape of a stumbling shoe, the beat of a racing heart, the swallow of a dry throat — all could originate from Violet and her captor, a gruff knight named Alaric, or from a demon lurking in the dark.

5   A prod from behind sent terror as sharp as a sword piercing through a silent Violet, and she struggled to stifle a scream. Relief washed over her when she realised it was only Alaric.

"Faster," he whispered. "You want to salvage the reputation of your kind by proving magic can be used for good, yes? Find the herb that remedies all ills and the king will free you and cease persecuting your fellow witches." But, despite his aggression, Alaric couldn't conceal the tremor in his voice.

10   Biting back her disbelief, Violet maintained a snail-like speed as she traversed the labyrinth, trailing her hand along the wall for a semblance of balance. Though the temptation to light a flame was strong, since the magic in her veins rendered rocks or kindling unnecessary, Violet resisted. Introducing a light to the darkness was a danger, as the darkness might wish to remain alone.

They shuffled onwards, their perception of time skewed, their precise location unknown.

15 Suddenly, the wall that Violet was so reliant upon came to an abrupt end, leaving her fingers grasping at empty air. She froze, unwilling to take another step for fear of losing all sense of direction entirely. They were approaching a trap — she could sense it.

Answer these questions about the text that you've just read.
Circle the letter of the correct answer.

1. What are Violet and Alaric searching for?

   A   A way out of the tunnels
   B   A plant that will cure every sickness
   C   Some of Violet's fellow witches
   D   A demon that lives in the tunnels
   E   Some fire to light the way

2. Which of the following is not a way that the darkness affects Violet?

   A   She becomes suspicious of ordinary noises.
   B   She starts to lose track of time.
   C   She can't work out where she is.
   D   She struggles to keep her balance.
   E   She becomes able to hear better.

/ 2

Carry on to the next question → →

3. Which of the following statements is false?

   A Alaric and Violet are trying to be quiet.
   B It doesn't take long for Violet to fear the tunnels.
   C There is no light in the tunnels.
   D Violet is being held in the tunnels partly against her will.
   E Alaric isn't scared of being in the tunnels.

4. What sound does Violet not hear as she walks through the tunnels?

   A A fast heartbeat
   B The voice of a demon
   C A swallowing sound
   D Alaric speaking
   E Somebody tripping up

5. What has the king promised Violet if she is successful in the tunnels?

   A He will accept her into the royal household.
   B She will be able to teach others how to do magic.
   C Witches won't be treated badly anymore.
   D She will become known as the most powerful witch.
   E The tunnels will become hers.

6. Which of the following best describes how Violet feels about the king's promises?

   A She is hopeful about them.
   B She is confident in them.
   C She is worried about them.
   D She doesn't agree with them.
   E She doesn't trust them.

7. Which of the following statements is true?

   A Violet and Alaric are moving through the tunnels slowly.
   B Violet needs wood to start a fire.
   C Alaric is patient with Violet.
   D Violet thinks lighting up the tunnels is a good idea.
   E Alaric is walking ahead of Violet.

8. Why does Violet panic when she can no longer feel the wall?

   A She suspects that Alaric has led her into a trap.
   B She thinks a demon made the wall disappear.
   C She won't be able to tell which way she's going.
   D She thinks the tunnels are caving in.
   E She thinks she is going to fall over and hurt herself.

/ 6

Answer these questions about the way words and phrases are used in the passage.

9. Which of these words is closest in meaning to "stifle" (line 6)?

    A Deny
    B Suppress
    C Resist
    D Overcome
    E Contain

10. What is meant by the word "salvage" (line 7)?

    A Protect
    B Improve
    C Reinforce
    D Save
    E Alter

11. In the line "leaving her fingers grasping at empty air" (lines 16-17), which word is an adjective?

    A leaving
    B her
    C fingers
    D at
    E empty

12. What type of words are these?
    originate   proving   conceal

    A Adverbs
    B Adjectives
    C Verbs
    D Conjunctions
    E Nouns

13. "They shuffled onwards, their perception of time skewed" (line 14). This contains an example of:

    A personification.
    B onomatopoeia.
    C a simile.
    D a cliché.
    E a metaphor.

14. "The gloom taunted them, once-harmless sounds becoming ominous." (line 2)
    Which technique is used here?

    A An analogy
    B Alliteration
    C A simile
    D Onomatopoeia
    E Personification

/ 6

Carry on to the next question → →

Assessment Test 5

> Read this passage carefully and answer the questions that follow.

An adapted extract from 'The Golden Age'

Colt-like I ran through the meadows, frisking happy heels in the face of Nature. Above, the sky was bluest of the blue; wide pools left by the winter's floods flashed the colour back, true and brilliant and the soft air thrilled with the germinating touch that seemed to kindle something in my own small person as well as in the rash primrose already lurking in sheltered haunts. Out into the brimming
5 sun-bathed world I sped, free of lessons, free of discipline and correction, for one day at least. My legs ran of themselves, and though I heard my name called faint and shrill behind, there was no stopping for me. It was only Harold, I concluded, and his legs, though shorter than mine, were good for a longer spurt than this. Then I heard it called again, but this time more faintly, with a pathetic break in the middle and I pulled up short, recognising Charlotte's plaintive note.

10 She panted up shortly, and dropped on the turf beside me. Neither had any desire for talk; the glow and the glory of existing on this perfect morning were satisfaction full and sufficient.

"Where's Harold?" I asked presently.

"Oh, he's just playin' muffin-man, as usual," said Charlotte with petulance. "Fancy wanting to be a muffin-man on a whole holiday!"

15 It was a strange craze, certainly, but Harold, who invented his own games and played them without assistance, always stuck staunchly to a new fad, till he had worn it quite out. Just at present he was a muffin-man, and day and night he went through passages and up and down staircases, ringing a noiseless bell and offering phantom muffins to invisible wayfarers. It sounds a poor sort of sport and yet — to pass along busy streets of your own building, for ever ringing an imaginary bell and
20 offering airy muffins of your own make to a bustling thronging crowd of your own creation — there were points about the game, it cannot be denied, though it seemed scarce in harmony with this radiant wind-swept morning!

by Kenneth Grahame

> Answer these questions about the text that you've just read.
> Circle the letter of the correct answer.

15. Which of these is not mentioned in the passage?

   A Where the narrator is.
   B The time of day.
   C How loud Charlotte's voice sounds.
   D Why the children aren't at school.
   E The narrator's name.

16. What colour do the "wide pools" (line 2) appear?

   A White
   B Black
   C Green
   D Blue
   E Purple

(/ 2)

17. What did the narrator do when they first heard someone call after them?

    A They stopped running.
    B They called back.
    C They kept running.
    D They slowed down.
    E They ran faster.

18. Which word best describes Charlotte's voice in lines 8-9?

    A Sarcastic
    B Frustrated
    C Enthusiastic
    D Resentful
    E Sorrowful

19. When they stopped running, why didn't the narrator and Charlotte speak straight away?

    A They were happy to just enjoy the day for a while.
    B They were both out of breath after running.
    C They were preoccupied looking for Harold.
    D They had fallen out with one another.
    E Charlotte was cross with the narrator.

20. Which of the following statements best describes the narrator's attitude towards Harold's game?

    A They thought it was inventive and wished they had thought of it themselves.
    B They thought it was peculiar but understood its merits.
    C They thought it was ridiculous and didn't understand Harold's enjoyment of it.
    D They thought it was childish and would be embarrassed to play it.
    E They thought it was boring and had no redeeming qualities.

21. Which word best describes Harold's approach to new fads?

    A Committed
    B Harmful
    C Incomprehensible
    D Nonchalant
    E Uninterested

22. Which of the following best describes the weather conditions in the passage?

    A Sunny and still
    B Cold and windy
    C Sunny and windy
    D Wet and windy
    E Sunny and cloudy

/ 6

Carry on to the next question → →

Answer these questions about the way words and phrases are used in the passage.

23. What is meant by the word "lurking" (line 4)?

   A   Hiding
   B   Trembling
   C   Recoiling
   D   Creeping
   E   Resting

24. Which of these is closest in meaning to the word "petulance" (line 13)?

   A   Boredom
   B   Excitement
   C   Jealousy
   D   Disbelief
   E   Sulkiness

25. The word "phantom" (line 18) could most accurately be replaced by:

   A   shadowy.
   B   petrifying.
   C   haunted.
   D   imaginary.
   E   menacing.

26. What is meant by the word "harmony" (line 21)?

   A   Approval
   B   Agreement
   C   Respect
   D   Empathy
   E   Precision

27. What type of word is "kindle" (line 3)?

   A   Noun
   B   Adjective
   C   Verb
   D   Adverb
   E   Pronoun

28. "up and down staircases, ringing a noiseless bell" (lines 17-18).
    Which are the two nouns in this phrase?

   A   "up" and "down"
   B   "staircases" and "bell"
   C   "ringing" and "noiseless"
   D   "noiseless" and "bell"
   E   "staircases" and "ringing"

/ 6

In this passage, there are some punctuation mistakes. Circle the letter which matches the part of the sentence with the mistake. If there's no mistake, circle N.

29. Kai was on his way to watch a great spectacle the annual hot air balloon festival.
    A   B   C   D   N

30. "Do you know how many hot air balloons there will be? Kai asked his dad.
    A   B   C   D   N

31. "I've heard therell be over 100!" Kai's dad responded. As they approached the festival,
    A   B   C   D   N

32. the faint-sound of music grew louder and Kai's excitement for the day ahead
    A   B   C   D   N

33. started to soar. A few seconds later, Kai caught a glimpse of a balloon as green
    A   B   C   D   N

34. as a lime a yellow, purple and blue balloon; and another that was silver and gold.
    A   B   C   D   N

/ 6

Choose the right word or phrase to complete the passage.
Circle the letter which matches the correct word.

35. Owning chickens requires a lot **in as of by if** careful consideration, so do your research
                                      A   B   C   D   E

36. **among apart except before to** adopting them. First, you need to make sure you
      A   B   C   D   E

37. **has have had having hasn't** enough space to house them. It's a good idea to have a
     A   B   C   D   E

38. nesting box **filled fill filling fills fillings** with hay so they will be more comfortable.
                   A   B   C   D   E

39. **Meanwhile Whenever Subsequently Although Wherever** every chicken is different,
      A   B   C   D   E

40. on **averaged averaging average averages averagely** a hen will lay one egg per day.
          A   B   C   D   E

/ 6

Carry on to the next question → →

Assessment Test 5

In this passage, there are some spelling mistakes. Circle the letter which matches the part of the sentence with the mistake. If there's no mistake, circle N.

41. Rory and his brother Oliver desided to bury a time capsule in their garden for
    A   B   C   D   N

42. people to discover in the future. They dug a hole rughly the size of a shoe box next
    A   B   C   D   N

43. to an apple tree. Rory wrote a letter to go inside the box, explaining who they were
    A   B   C   D   N

44. alongside their predictians for what society would be like in the future. They also
    A   B   C   D   N

45. put a photograph of the two of them inside, with their names and ages scrawled on
    A   B   C   D   N

46. the back. Oliver drew a map to show the exact locacion of the time capsule and hid
    A   B   C   D   N

47. it under the stairs in a cubboard. Two hundred years later, the Singh family stumbled
    A   B   C   D   N

48. upon a dust-covered book whilst rennovating their house. Cautiously peeling the pages
    A   B   C   D   N

49. open revealed what appeared to be a treasure map. They grabbed a spade and
    A   B   C   D   N

50. headed out into the garden, the suspence mounting at what they might unearth.
    A   B   C   D   N

/ 10

Total / 50

End of Test

Assessment Test 6

Allow 50 minutes to do this test and work as quickly and as carefully as you can.

You can print **multiple-choice answer sheets** for these questions from our website —
go to cgpbooks.co.uk/11plus/answer-sheets or scan the QR code on the right. If you'd
prefer to answer the questions on the page, just follow the instructions in the question.

Answer
Sheets

> Read this passage carefully and answer the questions that follow.

The Book vs. Television Debate

Since the 1950s, there has been a monumental rise in the popularity of television. Statistics show
that over 90 percent of UK households now own a minimum of one TV, with the average viewer
spending at least three hours a day glued to a screen. However, despite the staggering success of
television, a significant number of people claim that it remains inferior to books.

5   It may seem absurd to suggest that the traditional novel could triumph over the state-of-the-art
television, with its crystal-clear images and immersive audio. However, books allow readers to
conjure their own unique visualisations of stories, offering an escape from reality that is proven to be
effective in reducing stress. Equally, by engaging with the text to bring it to life, readers' vocabularies
tend to improve, assisting them in their learning at school and beyond.

10   Admittedly, TV can also be educational. While reading a book can take days, shorter television
episodes allow viewers to consume information quickly and efficiently. In under an hour, viewers can
expand their horizons by witnessing unfamiliar spectacles and following the stories of people whose
lives are wholly unlike theirs. This exposure to a multitude of locations and cultures from around the
globe can encourage viewers to develop a greater understanding and acceptance of others.

15   Therefore, although books and television may seem to be rivals, their merits in fact show them to
be two sides of the same coin — one valuable in deepening our relationship with the world around us.

> Answer these questions about the text that you've just read.
> Circle the letter of the correct answer.

1. According to the text, which of the following statements about books is false?

   A Reading books can help people to feel more relaxed.
   B Books offer readers a lot of creative freedom.
   C Readers have their own versions of what the world in the story looks like.
   D It often takes longer to read a book than to watch something on television.
   E Reading is proven to be more educational than watching television.

2. Why does the author say "It may seem absurd" (line 5) to say books are better than television?

   A The stories in books aren't as enjoyable as those on television.
   B More people own televisions than books.
   C Televisions are a newer invention than books.
   D Televisions have more features than books.
   E Television is more successful than books.

/ 2

Carry on to the next question → →

3. According to the text, why can watching television be educational?

   A You can see things that you haven't experienced before.
   B Hearing as well as seeing content helps you to remember it.
   C You can hear a more diverse range of vocabulary.
   D You can learn about places that aren't written about in books.
   E The faster you learn information, the longer you remember it.

4. Which of the following features of television is not mentioned in the text?

   A The quality of the images on the screen
   B The effect that the sound has on the viewer
   C The amount of the screen the images fill
   D Whether the places shown are always familiar
   E Whether a large range of cultures is shown

5. According to the text, what is positive about books compared to television?

   A There are no pictures, so readers are given more information.
   B Books contain a lot more detail so readers can understand more.
   C Books use more complicated vocabulary, which makes them more interesting.
   D Readers can read between the lines to understand the story.
   E Readers can use their imaginations to picture the story.

6. Which of the following is not mentioned in the text?

   A When television started becoming popular.
   B What percentage of UK households own a television.
   C Why television has increased in popularity.
   D Whether the popularity of television has grown significantly.
   E How long the average person watches television for in a day.

7. According to the text, which of these statements is true?

   A On average, people spend more time reading than watching television.
   B Books can be a valuable learning tool.
   C Television is used more than books to help with learning in schools.
   D Stories tend to be explained better in books than on television.
   E Information on television is presented too quickly for children to understand.

8. According to the text, what do books and television have in common?

   A They provide information that puts an end to various debates.
   B They make people question their beliefs.
   C They give us advice about how to get on with other people.
   D They give responses to unanswered questions.
   E They help us to understand the world better.

(/ 6)

Answer these questions about the way words and phrases are used in the passage.

9. Which of these words is closest in meaning to "staggering" (line 3)?

    A Precarious
    B Unsteady
    C Dramatic
    D Astonishing
    E Unexpected

10. Which of these words is closest in meaning to "witnessing" (line 12)?

    A Questioning
    B Inspecting
    C Considering
    D Welcoming
    E Observing

11. Which of these words is closest in meaning to "merits" (line 15)?

    A Attributes
    B Similarities
    C Benefits
    D Descriptions
    E Uses

12. What type of words are these?
remains   triumph   improve

    A Adverbs
    B Prepositions
    C Adjectives
    D Verbs
    E Conjunctions

13. Which of the following lines contains personification?

    A "a monumental rise in the popularity of television" (line 1)
    B "a significant number of people claim that it remains inferior" (line 4)
    C "the traditional novel could triumph over the state-of-the-art television" (lines 5-6)
    D "readers' vocabularies tend to improve" (lines 8-9)
    E "deepening our relationship with the world around us" (line 16)

14. What is meant by the phrase "viewers can expand their horizons" (lines 11-12)?

    A Viewers can disregard what they have already learned.
    B Viewers can see the world in a more positive light.
    C Viewers can learn information that people don't generally know about.
    D Viewers can experience and learn about new things.
    E Viewers can try out different lifestyles.

/ 6

Carry on to the next question → →

Read this poem carefully and answer the questions that follow.

June Sunset

Here shall my heart find its haven of calm,
By rush-fringed rivers and rain-fed streams
That glimmer thro' meadows of lily and palm.
Here shall my soul find its true repose
5   Under a sunset sky of dreams
Diaphanous*, amber and rose.
The air is aglow with the glint and whirl
Of swift wild wings in their homeward flight,
Sapphire, emerald, topaz, and pearl.
10   Afloat in the evening light.

A brown quail* cries from the tamarisk bushes,
A bulbul* calls from the cassia*-plume,
And thro' the wet earth the gentian* pushes
Her spikes of silvery bloom.
15   Where'er the foot of the bright shower passes
Fragrant and fresh delights unfold;
The wild fawns feed on the scented grasses,
Wild bees on the cactus-gold.

An ox-cart stumbles upon the rocks,
20   And a wistful music pursues the breeze
From a shepherd's pipe as he gathers his flocks
Under the *pipal*-trees.
And a young *Banjara** driving her cattle
Lifts up her voice as she glitters by
25   In an ancient ballad of love and battle
Set to the beat of a mystic tune,
And the faint stars gleam in the eastern sky
To herald a rising moon.

by Sarojini Naidu

*Diaphanous — *delicate and see-through*   *quail — *a small bird*   *bulbul — *a songbird*
*cassia — *a type of tree*   *gentian — *a type of flower*   *Banjara — *a person from the Banjara tribe*

Answer these questions about the text that you've just read.
Circle the letter of the correct answer.

15. Which word best describes how the narrator feels as they watch the sunset?

   A   Restless
   B   Lovesick
   C   Overwhelmed
   D   Peaceful
   E   Conflicted

16. Which of the following is not mentioned by the narrator in lines 1-14?

   A   The colour of the rivers
   B   The colour of the sky
   C   The colour of the birds in the sky
   D   The colour of the quail
   E   The colour of the gentian flowers

/ 2

17. Where are the birds flying in lines 7-10?

   A Towards the sunset
   B Towards the narrator
   C Up into the sky
   D Into the meadows
   E Towards their nests

18. What are the "Wild bees" doing in line 18?

   A Buzzing loudly
   B Collecting food from flowers
   C Chasing the fawns
   D Flying through the grass
   E Building a hive on a cactus

19. Who or what is making the "music" described in line 20?

   A A cart clattering on rocks
   B A flock of sheep
   C An instrument being played
   D The wind in the trees
   E A woman singing

20. What is the "bright shower" most likely to be in line 15?

   A The bees
   B The birds
   C The rain
   D The sun
   E The fawns

21. According to the poem, what role do the stars play?

   A They separate the east from the west.
   B They light up the moon.
   C They light up the land below.
   D They signal the end of the sunset.
   E They signal the arrival of the moon.

22. According to the poem, which of the following statements is true?

   A The young *Banjara* is riding on a cow.
   B The narrator can hear the young *Banjara* but can't see her.
   C The young *Banjara* is singing a song she wrote herself.
   D The young *Banjara*'s song tells a story.
   E The young *Banjara* is playing a drum.

/ 6

Carry on to the next question → →

Assessment Test 6

Answer these questions about the way words and phrases are used in the passage.

23. Which of these words is closest in meaning to "haven" (line 1)?

   A Moment
   B Journey
   C Longing
   D Refuge
   E Paradise

24. The word "wistful" (line 20) could be most accurately replaced by:

   A triumphant.
   B melancholy.
   C faint.
   D catchy.
   E enchanting.

25. What is meant by the phrase "Lifts up her voice" (line 24)?

   A Looks up at the sky
   B Sings a higher note
   C Calls out loudly
   D Speaks more loudly
   E Starts to sing

26. "The air is aglow with the glint and whirl / Of swift wild wings in their homeward flight" (lines 7-8).
    What type of word is "whirl"?

   A Noun
   B Adjective
   C Adverb
   D Verb
   E Pronoun

27. "And the faint stars gleam in the eastern sky" (line 27).
    Which of these words is a verb?

   A faint
   B stars
   C gleam
   D eastern
   E sky

28. "Fragrant and fresh delights unfold" (line 16).
    What technique is being used here?

   A Onomatopoeia
   B Analogy
   C Simile
   D Personification
   E Alliteration

/ 6

In this passage, there are some spelling mistakes. Circle the letter which matches the part of the sentence with the mistake. If there's no mistake, circle N.

29. Located off the north coast of Scotland, the Orkney Islands are the perfect holiday

        A   B   C   D   N

30. destinasion for both nature and history enthusiasts. A visit to the famous UNESCO

        A   B   C   D   N

31. World Heritage Site, which includes many spectacular prehistoric monumants, is a must.

        A   B   C   D   N

32. Anually, Orkney receives nearly 200 000 visitors, which isn't surprising given the

        A   B   C   D   N

33. abundance of activities to experience. It's easy to access Orkney — conveniently, there

        A   B   C   D   N

34. are airports and ferry terminals across the islands. Plan you're visit to Orkney today!

        A   B   C   D   N

/ 6

In this passage, there are some punctuation mistakes. Circle the letter which matches the part of the sentence with the mistake. If there's no mistake, circle N.

Dear Diary,

35. We spent our first day in New york City at the Museum of Modern Art. My favourite

        A   B   C   D   N

36. painting was *The Starry Night* by Van Gogh, which was painted in 1889. A crowd

        A   B   C   D   N

37. was huddled around it — it's a very famous artwork but once we got to the front,

        A   B   C   D   N

38. it was worth the wait. Van Gogh made a variety of impressive oil paintings drawings,

        A   B   C   D   N

39. watercolour's and sketches over his lifetime (specifically between 1880 and 1890).

        A   B   C   D   N

40. Will we see more incredible art while we're here. I really hope so!

        A   B   C   D   N

/ 6

Carry on to the next question → →

Assessment Test 6

Choose the right word or phrase to complete the passage.
Circle the letter which matches the correct word.

41. **Now   Next   Last   Today   Late**   night I made a gingerbread house.
    A   B   C   D   E

42. I   **follow   following   follows   followed   follower**   a new recipe to make the
    A   B   C   D   E

43. gingerbread biscuits. After they'd finished baking   **on   in   over   with   to**   the oven,
    A   B   C   D   E

44. I left them to cool. If I hadn't let them cool, they   **had   can   will   would   must**   have
    A   B   C   D   E

45. crumbled when I decorated them.   **Once   Since   Until   While   If**   I'd decorated
    A   B   C   D   E

46. the biscuits, I glued them into a house shape   **about   as   within   by   with**   icing.
    A   B   C   D   E

47. **Consequently   After   However   Despite   Instead**   I'd finished this, I dusted the house
    A   B   C   D   E

48. with icing sugar to   **makes   making   made   maker   make**   it look like it had snowed.
    A   B   C   D   E

49. I showed my mum, who   **taken   takes   took   take   taking**   several photographs. I was
    A   B   C   D   E

50. so   **pleased   please   pleasing   pleases   pleaser**   with the result. It looked delicious!
    A   B   C   D   E

/ 10

Total   / 50

End of Test

Glossary

abbreviation	A <u>shortened version</u> of a word, e.g. "<u>Ave</u>" instead of "<u>Avenue</u>".
adjective	A word that <u>describes</u> a <u>noun</u>, e.g. "<u>grey</u> sky", "<u>fast</u> car".
adverb	A word that <u>describes</u> a <u>verb</u> or an <u>adjective</u>, e.g. "She fought <u>bravely</u>."
alliteration	The <u>repetition</u> of a <u>sound</u> at the beginning of words within a phrase, e.g. "<u>F</u>reddie <u>f</u>eeds on <u>f</u>lies."
antonym	A word that has the <u>opposite meaning</u> to another, e.g. "<u>hot</u>" and "<u>cold</u>".
comparative	A word that <u>compares</u> one thing with another, e.g. "<u>longer</u>", "<u>better</u>".
conjunction	A word that <u>joins</u> two clauses, e.g. "<u>and</u>", "<u>but</u>".
fiction	Text that has been <u>made up</u> by the author, about <u>imaginary people</u> and <u>events</u>.
homographs	Words that are <u>spelt the same</u>, but have <u>different meanings</u>, e.g. <u>bear</u> (animal/endure).
homophones	Words that <u>sound the same</u>, but mean different things, e.g. "<u>new</u>" and "<u>knew</u>".
idiom	A phrase which <u>doesn't literally mean</u> what it <u>says</u>, e.g. "a piece of cake".
imagery	Language that creates a <u>vivid picture</u> in the reader's mind.
irony	When a writer says the <u>opposite</u> of what they <u>mean</u>, or when the <u>opposite happens</u> to what the reader <u>expects</u>.
metaphor	A way of <u>describing</u> something by saying that it <u>is</u> something else, e.g. "The children's smiles were beacons of light."
non-fiction	Text that is about <u>facts</u> and <u>real people</u> and <u>events</u>.
noun	A word that <u>names</u> something, e.g. "<u>Jayden</u>", "<u>pencil</u>", "<u>team</u>", "<u>love</u>".
onomatopoeia	When words <u>sound</u> like the <u>noise</u> they describe, e.g. "<u>crack</u>", "<u>hiss</u>", "<u>fizz</u>".
personification	A way of describing something by giving it <u>human feelings</u> and <u>characteristics</u>, e.g. "The tree quivered fearfully as the blackbird landed on the branch."
prefix	Letters that can be put <u>in front</u> of a word to <u>change its meaning</u>, e.g. "<u>re</u>play".
preposition	A word that tells you how things are <u>related</u>, e.g. "<u>at</u>", "<u>under</u>", "<u>before</u>", "<u>with</u>".
pronoun	Words that can be used <u>instead</u> of <u>nouns</u>, e.g. "<u>I</u>", "<u>you</u>", "<u>we</u>", "<u>they</u>".
proverb	A short, well-known saying that may <u>give advice</u>, e.g. "Actions speak louder than words."
rhetorical question	A question that <u>doesn't</u> need an <u>answer</u>, e.g. "How many times do I have to tell you?"
simile	A way of describing something by <u>comparing</u> it to something else, e.g. "Her kindness was <u>like</u> a warm mug of hot chocolate on a cold day."
subject	The <u>person</u> or <u>thing doing</u> the action of a verb, e.g. "<u>Olive</u> danced", "<u>the lion</u> roared".
subordinate clause	A <u>less important</u> bit of the sentence which <u>doesn't make sense</u> on its own.
suffix	Letters that can be put <u>after</u> a word to <u>change its meaning</u>, e.g. "sad<u>ness</u>".
superlative	A word that refers to the <u>most</u> or <u>least</u> of a group of things, e.g. "the <u>greatest</u> city".
synonym	A word with a <u>similar meaning</u> to another word, e.g. "<u>small</u>" and "<u>tiny</u>".
verb	An <u>action</u> or <u>being</u> word, e.g. "I <u>swim</u>", "she <u>shouted</u>", "you <u>see</u>".

Answers

Section One — Grammar

Page 2 — Parts of Speech

1) **abstract noun** — 'distance' is an abstract noun because it is a name for something you can't experience with your five senses.

2) **common noun** — 'ants' is a common noun because it is a name for an object — it is in the plural form here.

3) **proper noun** — 'Karim' is a proper noun because it is the name of a person.

4) **abstract noun** — 'heat' is an abstract noun because it is a name for something you can't experience with your five senses.

5) **abstract noun** — 'ovation' is an abstract noun because it is a name for something you can't experience with your five senses.

6) **collective noun** — 'bunch' is a collective noun because it is the name for a group of keys.

7) **common noun** — 'hall' is a common noun because it is a name for an object.

8) **collective noun** — 'band' is a collective noun because it is the name for a group of musicians.

9) **collective noun** — 'congregation' is a collective noun because it is the name for a group of worshippers.

10) **onto** — 'onto' is a preposition because it describes where the vase was in relation to the floor after it fell.

11) **prepared** — 'prepared' is an adjective here because it describes the noun in the sentence — 'students'.

12) **rapidly** — 'rapidly' is an adverb because it describes how the fire spread.

13) **outside** — 'outside' is a preposition here because it describes where the crowd was in relation to the court.

14) **carefully** — 'carefully' is an adverb because it describes how Yan squeezed through the gap in the wall.

15) **daily** — 'daily' is an adjective here because it describes the noun in the sentence — 'exercises'.

16) **in** — 'in' is a preposition here because it describes where Grace put the note.

17) **clear** — 'clear' is an adjective here because it describes the noun in the sentence — 'signs'.

18) **late** — 'late' is an adverb here because it describes how Peter arrived.

Page 3 — Parts of Speech

1) **even though** — 'even though' makes the most sense in the sentence.

2) **before** — 'before' makes the most sense in the sentence.

3) **when** — 'when' makes the most sense in the sentence.

4) **so** — 'so' makes the most sense in the sentence.

5) **because** — 'because' makes the most sense in the sentence.

6) **why** — 'why' makes the most sense in the sentence.

7) **whether** — 'whether' makes the most sense in the sentence.

8) **while** — 'while' makes the most sense in the sentence.

9) **whereas** — 'whereas' makes the most sense in the sentence.

10) **she prefers netball** — 'she prefers netball' is a main clause because it makes sense on its own.

11) **The chef prepared a casserole** — 'The chef prepared a casserole' is a main clause because it makes sense on its own.

12) **when the announcement was made** — 'when the announcement was made' is a subordinate clause because it doesn't make sense on its own.

13) **The lemurs escaped** — 'The lemurs escaped' is a main clause because it makes sense on its own.

14) **unless she chooses the route** — 'unless she chooses the route' is a subordinate clause because it doesn't make sense on its own.

15) **they look much neater** — 'they look much neater' is a main clause because it makes sense on its own.

16) **so that everyone could see her** — 'so that everyone could see her' is a subordinate clause because it doesn't make sense on its own.

17) **The tanker ran aground** — 'The tanker ran aground' is a main clause because it makes sense on its own.

18) **If anybody opens the front door** — 'If anybody opens the front door' is a subordinate clause because it doesn't make sense on its own.

Page 4 — Verbs

1) **brushes** — 'brushes' is the verb in this sentence because it is the action word.

2) **peered** — 'peered' is the verb in this sentence because it is the action word.

3) **missed** — 'missed' is the verb in this sentence because it is the action word.

4) **parted** — 'parted' is the verb in this sentence because it is the action word.

5) **photographs** — 'photographs' is the verb in this sentence because it is the action word.

6) **were** — 'were' is the verb in this sentence because it describes a state of being.

7) **heard** — 'heard' is the verb in this sentence because it is the action word.

8) **thrive** — 'thrive' is the verb in this sentence because it is the action word.

9) **stifled** — 'stifled' is the verb in this sentence because it is the action word.

10) **shake** — The sentence should be 'The trees in the forest shake in the strong wind.' This is the correct present tense form of the verb 'to shake' and agrees with the subject — 'The trees'.

11) **was** — The sentence should be 'There was an elderly man waiting outside the bank when it opened.' This is the correct past tense form of the verb 'to be' and agrees with the subject — 'an elderly man'.

12) **fallen** — The sentence should be 'The cat had fallen from the highest branch, but it wasn't injured.' This is the correct option to complete the verb phrase 'had fallen'.

13) **tumbles** — The sentence should be 'The marble tumbles down the long flight of stairs.' This is the correct present tense form of the verb 'to tumble' and agrees with the subject — 'The marble'.

14) **was** — The sentence should be 'Harry was working at his desk when he heard the exciting news.' This is the correct option to complete the verb phrase 'was working' and agrees with the subject — 'Harry'. The second half of the sentence is in the past tense, so you need 'was' not 'is' to match this tense.

15) **were** — The sentence should be 'If you were to come to the party, what time would you arrive?' This sentence is about something that isn't necessarily real or true, so the subjunctive 'were' is correct.

16) **had** — The sentence should be 'She had run three miles before her left knee started to ache.' This is the correct option to complete the verb phrase 'had run'. The second half of the sentence is in the past tense, so you need 'had' not 'has' to match this tense.

17) **Stop** — The sentence should be 'Stop playing football when you hear the referee's whistle.' This is an instruction so 'Stop' is the only option that fits the sentence.

18) **remain** — The sentence should be 'I ask that you all remain seated until the ride stops.' This is the correct subjunctive form of the verb 'to remain'. The sentence is about the future so you need 'remain', not 'remained'.

Page 5 — Verbs

1) **pictures** — 'pictures' is the object in this sentence because 'My uncle Arthur', the subject of the sentence, is doing the action to the pictures.

2) **Shen** — 'Shen' is the subject in this sentence because he is doing the action — 'developed'.

3) **her car** — 'her car' is the object in this sentence because 'Mrs Bartlett', the subject of the sentence, is doing the action to it.

4) **the presenter** — 'the presenter' is the subject in this sentence because they are doing the action — 'revealed'.

5) **pupils** — 'pupils' is the subject in this sentence because the pupils are doing the action — 'played'.

6) **the document** — 'the document' is the object in this sentence because 'My cousins', the subject of the sentence, are doing the action to it.

7) **the cat** — 'the cat' is the object in this sentence because 'Aarvi', the subject of the sentence, is doing the action to it.

8) **I** — 'I' is the subject in this sentence because the person represented by the pronoun 'I' is doing the action — 'visited'.

9) **the thief** — 'the thief' is the object in this sentence because 'The lawyer', the subject of the sentence, is doing the action to the thief.

10) **The fence was damaged by the storm.** — This is the correct passive version of the active sentence, because it uses the passive verb formation 'was damaged' and the sentence focuses on the action, not the subject.

11) **My broken tooth will be fixed by my dentist.** — This is the correct passive version of the active sentence, because it uses the passive verb formation 'will be fixed' and the sentence focuses on the action, not the subject.

12) **The dog's paw was bitten by our cat.** — This is the correct passive version of the active sentence, because it uses the passive verb formation 'was bitten' and the sentence focuses on the action, not the subject.

13) **The angry driver was detained by the police.** — This is the correct passive version of the active sentence, because it uses the passive verb formation 'was detained' and the sentence focuses on the action, not the subject.

14) **Their house is shaken by an earthquake.** — This is the correct passive version of the active sentence, because it uses the passive verb formation 'is shaken' and the sentence focuses on the action, not the subject.

Page 6 — Mixed Grammar Questions

1) **were** — 'was' should be 'were'.
2) **yours** — 'your' should be 'yours'.
3) **any** — 'no' should be 'any'.
4) **are** — 'is' should be 'are'.
5) **stolen** — 'stole' should be 'stolen'.
6) **which** — 'what' should be 'which'.
7) **my** — 'mine' should be 'my'.
8) **well** — 'good' should be 'well'.
9) **I** — 'me' should be 'I'.
10) **noun** — 'success' is a noun because it is a naming word.
11) **adverb** — 'briskly' is an adverb because it describes the way Kathryn walked.
12) **preposition** — 'around' is a preposition here because it tells you where the motorbike raced in relation to the corner.
13) **adverb** — 'warmly' is an adverb because it tells you how the shopkeeper smiled.
14) **adjective** — 'oily' is an adjective because it describes the noun, 'stain'.

15) **verb** — 'Look' is a verb here because it is an action word.

16) **preposition** — 'by' is a preposition here because it tells you where Toby put his pencils in relation to his exam paper.

17) **adjective** — 'better' is an adjective here because it describes the noun, 'results'.

18) **verb** — 'fasts' is a verb here because it is an action word.

Page 7 — Mixed Grammar Questions

1) **Gradually** — 'Gradually' is the adverb in this sentence.

2) **generosity** — 'generosity' is the abstract noun in this sentence.

3) **them** — 'them' is the pronoun in this sentence.

4) **unless** — 'unless' is the conjunction in this sentence.

5) **leapt** — 'leapt' is the verb in this sentence.

6) **cousin** — 'cousin' is the common noun in this sentence.

7) **winding** — 'winding' is the adjective in this sentence.

8) **usually** — 'usually' is the adverb in this sentence.

9) **at** — 'at' is the preposition in this sentence.

10) **largest** — The sentence should be 'Rosie took the largest apple of all from the fruit bowl.'

11) **gently** — The sentence should be 'Fiona stroked the newborn lamb gently.'

12) **does** — The sentence should be 'Carys does all the housework whereas John cooks every night.'

13) **when** — The sentence should be 'The door slammed when the wind blew suddenly.'

14) **avoid** — The sentence should be 'If I were you, I would avoid that street.'

15) **mine** — The sentence should be 'I told my parents that the late library books were mine.'

16) **steadily** — The sentence should be 'The snow fell steadily during the night.'

17) **Although** — The sentence should be 'Although the rain had stopped, it was very humid.'

18) **go** — The sentence should be 'Casey and her family often go skiing at Christmas.'

Section Two — Punctuation

Page 8 — Commas and Brackets

1) **(the loud one)** — The sentence should be 'One of my dogs (the loud one) has a habit of barking at squirrels.' The brackets contain extra information.

2) **(150 individuals)** — The sentence should be 'A crowd of people (150 individuals) were waiting to board the plane.' The brackets contain extra information.

3) **(his microphone)** — The sentence should be 'The singer dropped something important at the concert (his microphone).' The brackets contain extra information.

4) **(birds that have extremely long necks)** — The sentence should be 'Ostriches (birds that have extremely long necks) can run quickly.' The brackets contain an explanation.

5) **(football and basketball)** — The sentence should be 'Sumaya plays sports (football and basketball) with her brothers and sisters.' The brackets contain extra information.

6) **(at least ten)** — The sentence should be 'Lia went on the slide many times (at least ten) before she went home.' The brackets contain extra information.

7) **(a type of extreme weather)** — The sentence should be 'Rachel finds tornadoes (a type of extreme weather) fascinating.' The brackets contain an explanation.

8) **(a small cottage)** — The sentence should be 'My grandad's house (a small cottage) is very cosy in the winter.' The brackets contain extra information.

9) **(not me)** — The sentence should be 'Someone (not me) dropped a bowl of tomato soup on the white carpet.' The brackets contain extra information.

10) **jellyfish, dolphins** — The sentence should be 'The diver was mesmerised by the jellyfish, dolphins and sharks.' The comma separates a list of nouns.

11) **dismay, I** — The sentence should be 'To my dismay, I fell in the puddle and got totally drenched.' The comma separates the adverbial at the start of the sentence.

12) **Cairo, Egypt** — The sentence should be 'Nick is planning an exciting trip to Cairo, Egypt.' The comma separates the city from the country.

13) **protests, Maya** — The sentence should be 'Despite her mother's protests, Maya brought the snail inside.' The comma separates two clauses.

14) **Ikemba, an** — The sentence should be 'Ikemba, an avid reader, has read more than fifty books this year.' The pair of commas contain extra information.

15) **cake, which** — The sentence should be 'The cake, which was fresh out of the oven, had mysteriously disappeared.' The pair of commas contain extra information.

16) **shirt, gloves** — The sentence should be 'My spy outfit consisted of sunglasses, a dark shirt, gloves and black trousers.' The commas separate a list of nouns and noun phrases.

17) **sister, ice** — The sentence should be 'I usually take Gemma, my younger sister, ice skating on Saturdays.' The pair of commas contain extra information.

18) **forest, dark** — The sentence should be 'The forest, dark and eerie, was feared by all who heard about it.' The pair of commas contain extra information.

Page 9 — Dashes and Hyphens

1) **incorrect** — The sentence should be 'The puzzle — nearly impossible to solve — took us hours.' The dashes in the correct version of the sentence separate the extra information.

2) **correct** — The dash joins the two related main clauses.

3) **incorrect** — The sentence should be 'The milk chocolate — my favourite — melted in the sun.' The dashes in the correct version of the sentence separate the extra information.

4) **incorrect** — The sentence should be 'I named my kitten Shadow — she always follows me.' The dash in the correct version of the sentence joins the two related main clauses.

5) **correct** — The dash joins the two related main clauses.

6) **correct** — The dashes separate the extra information.

7) **incorrect** — The sentence should be 'The meadow looks lovely — it's filled with purple flowers.' The dash in the correct version of the sentence joins the two related main clauses.

8) **correct** — The dashes separate the extra information.

9) **incorrect** — The sentence should be 'The best place — though it's small — is my school's library.' The dashes in the correct version of the sentence separate the extra information.

10) **two-day** — The hyphen makes it clear that the trip was two days long.

11) **fresh-faced** — The hyphen shows that the word 'fresh' is describing the word 'faced', which makes it clear what Beatrice looks like.

12) **co-author** — The hyphen is used to join the prefix 'co' with the word 'author'.

13) **last-minute** — The hyphen makes it clear that the dash to the shops happened at the last minute.

14) **all-inclusive** — The hyphen is used to join the prefix 'all' with the word 'inclusive'.

15) **long-lost** — The hyphen shows that the word 'long' is describing the word 'lost', which makes it clear that the grandma hadn't seen her twin in a long time.

16) **French-speaking** — The hyphen makes it clear that the people at the school spoke French.

17) **blue-eyed** — The hyphen shows that the word 'blue' is describing the word 'eyed', which makes it clear that Tamara has blue eyes.

18) **child-friendly** — The hyphen makes it clear that the rollercoaster is suitable for children.

Page 10 — Apostrophes

1) **its** — 'its' is possessive so it doesn't need an apostrophe. It shows that the nest belongs to the bird.

2) **It's** — 'it's' is the shortened version of 'it is' so it needs an apostrophe.

3) **it's** — 'it's' is the shortened version of 'it is' so it needs an apostrophe.

4) **its** — 'its' is possessive so it doesn't need an apostrophe. It shows that the strings belong to the guitar.

5) **it's** — 'it's' is the shortened version of 'it is' so it needs an apostrophe.

6) **its** — 'its' is possessive so it doesn't need an apostrophe. It shows that the den belongs to the bear.

7) **it's** — 'it's' is the shortened version of 'it is' so it needs an apostrophe.

8) **its** — 'its' is possessive so it doesn't need an apostrophe. It shows that the screen belongs to the computer.

9) **it's** — 'it's' is the shortened version of 'it is' so it needs an apostrophe.

10) **Lilly's** — The possessive apostrophe goes before the 's' because there is only one Lilly.

11) **isn't** — 'isn't' is the shortened version of 'is not' — the apostrophe represents the missing letters.

12) **they've** — 'they've' is the shortened version of 'they have' — the apostrophe represents the missing letters.

13) **butterflies'** — The possessive apostrophe goes at the end of the word because 'butterflies' is plural and ends in 's'.

14) **hasn't** — 'hasn't' is the shortened version of 'has not' — the apostrophe represents the missing letters.

15) **Jacob's** — The possessive apostrophe goes before the 's' because there is only one Jacob.

16) **children's** — The possessive apostrophe goes before the 's' because 'children' is an irregular plural that doesn't end in 's'.

17) **mustn't** — 'mustn't' is the shortened version of 'must not' — the apostrophe represents the missing letters.

18) **cows'** — The possessive apostrophe goes at the end of the word because 'cows' is plural and ends in an 's'.

Page 11 — Inverted Commas, Colons and Semicolons

1) **"Din found a caterpillar," said Beth.**
Make sure you add a comma before the second set of inverted commas. Other variations are correct.

2) **"What time is it?" we asked.**
Make sure you add a question mark before the second set of inverted commas. Other variations are correct.

3) **"I won the lottery!" Diego exclaimed.**
Make sure you change 'he' to 'I' because Diego is talking about himself. Other variations are correct.

4) **"It might snow later," she speculated.**
Make sure you add a comma before the second set of inverted commas. Other variations are correct.

5) **"Keep a diary," Haru advised me.**
Make sure you add a comma before the second set of inverted commas. Other variations are correct.

6) **backpack: a book**
The sentence should be 'Put these things in your backpack: a book, some pencils and your lunch box.' This colon introduces a list.

7) friend; they

The sentence should be 'Zoey grinned when she saw her best friend; they had been apart for too long.' This semicolon joins two main clauses to make one sentence.

8) mission: to

The sentence should be 'Marcus had just one mission in life: to find the world's tastiest chocolate biscuits.' This colon introduces an explanation.

9) pets: a fluffy

The sentence should be 'Isabelle has three pets: a fluffy puppy, an excitable hamster and a timid cat.' This colon introduces a list.

10) hard; the

The sentence should be 'The actors worked extremely hard; the performance was a huge success.' This semicolon joins two main clauses to make one sentence.

11) old farm; the

The sentence should be 'I love visiting my dad's old farm; the lake near my school; and Aunt Jane's house.' The semicolons are used to separate phrases in a list.

12) relief; no

The sentence should be 'Julius breathed a sigh of relief; no one had seen him escape.' This semicolon joins two main clauses to make one sentence.

13) travel: by

The sentence should be 'There was only one way that Ron wanted to travel: by using a zipwire.' This colon introduces an explanation.

14) window; another

The sentence should be 'Fatima sprinted to the window; another shooting star whizzed past.' This semicolon joins two main clauses to make one sentence.

Page 12 — Mixed Punctuation Questions

1) "Would you like to go sledging with me?" asked Dylan.

Dylan is asking a question so there should be a question mark before the second set of inverted commas.

2) Timo pushed the snowball, which was rather large, down the steep hill.

There should be a comma between 'snowball' and 'which' to separate the extra information — 'which was rather large'.

3) "Please can I borrow the purple paint?" Amahle asked Freddy.

There should be a second set of inverted commas after the question mark — inverted commas always come in pairs.

4) There were expensive items in the box: a gold ring, diamonds and a necklace.

There should be a colon between 'box' and 'a' — the colon introduces a list.

5) An ancient coin, lost for a thousand years, has finally been unearthed.

There should be a comma between 'coin' and 'lost' to separate the extra information — 'lost for a thousand years'.

6) The ladies' table was reserved for ten o'clock in the morning.

There should be an apostrophe at the end of the word 'ladies' because the noun is plural and the apostrophe shows possession.

7) Clara's house (built in 1920) has a secret underground passageway.

There should be a closing bracket between '1920' and 'has' — brackets always come in pairs.

8) "Make sure you take lots of pictures," Dad advised me.

There should be a comma between 'pictures' and the second set of inverted commas.

9) In the summer, sweet-smelling flowers bloom in my garden.

There should be a hyphen that joins the words 'sweet' and 'smelling' — the hyphen makes it clear that the flowers smell sweet.

10) It's nearly time to drive to Scotland.

'Its' should be 'It's' — 'it's' is a shortened version of 'it is' so it needs an apostrophe. 'scotland' should be 'Scotland' — it is a proper noun.

11) "I can't believe that happened," laughed Reece.

'cant' should be 'can't' — the apostrophe shows where the words have been shortened and the 'n' and 'o' are missing. 'Laughed' should be 'laughed' — it is still part of the same sentence.

12) You need these items: glue, paper and glitter.

The comma after 'items' should be a colon — colons are used to introduce a list. There should be a comma between 'paper' and 'glue' too — this is to separate items in a list.

13) Helen — a world-famous author — lives there.

There should be a dash between 'Helen' and 'a' to separate the extra information — 'a world-famous author'. 'world famous' should be 'world-famous' — the hyphen makes it clear that the author is famous around the world.

Page 13 — Mixed Punctuation Questions

1) "We have got to find the last item and win the scavenger hunt," said Bobby. His team had found three things on the list: some chalk, a tennis ball and a book about insects.

The bits that are underlined show where punctuation has been added. You get one mark for each of the following: opening inverted commas before 'We'; a capital letter at the beginning of 'We'; a comma after 'hunt'; closing inverted commas after 'hunt,'; a capital letter at the beginning of 'Bobby'; a full stop after 'Bobby'; a capital letter at the beginning of 'His'; a colon after 'list'; a comma after 'chalk'; a full stop after 'insects'.

2) Like whippets, they scampered into the forest. Gradually, Bobby's short-lived confidence turned into mild despair when he realised his team's chances were low.

The bits that are underlined show where punctuation has been added. You get one mark for each of the following: a capital letter at the beginning of 'Like'; a comma after 'whippets'; a full stop after 'forest'; a capital letter at the beginning of 'Gradually'; a comma after 'Gradually'; a capital letter at the beginning of 'Bobby's'; an apostrophe in 'Bobby's'; a hyphen joining 'short' and 'lived'; an apostrophe in 'team's'; a full stop after 'low'.

3) "Has anyone seen any sign of a pink flower yet?" Bobby asked in an urgent voice. His team, dirty from searching through piles of mud and leaves, shook their heads.

The bits that are underlined show where punctuation has been added. You get one mark for each of the following: opening inverted commas before 'Has'; a capital letter at the beginning of 'Has'; a question mark after 'yet'; closing inverted commas after 'yet?'; a capital letter at the beginning of 'Bobby'; a full stop after 'voice'; a capital letter at the beginning of 'His'; a comma after 'team'; a comma after 'leaves'; a full stop after 'heads'.

Section Three — Spelling

Page 14 — Plurals

1) **cities** — 'city' becomes 'cities'. When the letter before the 'y' is a consonant, 'ies' is added to make the plural.

2) **lives** — 'life' becomes 'lives'. Words ending in 'fe' lose the final 'fe' and add 'ves' to make the plural.

3) **chefs** — 'chef' becomes 'chefs'. This is different to most words ending in 'f' because only 's' is added to make the plural.

4) **berries** — 'berry' becomes 'berries'. When the letter before the 'y' is a consonant, 'ies' is added to make the plural.

5) **stitches** — 'stitch' becomes 'stitches'. Often words ending 'ch' add 'es' to make the plural.

6) **radios** — 'radio' becomes 'radios'. Some words ending in 'o' add 's' to make the plural.

7) **shelves** — 'shelf' becomes 'shelves'. Often words ending in 'f' lose the final 'f' and add 'ves' to make the plural.

8) **flashes** — 'flash' becomes 'flashes'. Words ending 'sh' add 'es' to make the plural.

9) **mosquitoes** — 'mosquito' becomes 'mosquitoes'. Some words ending in 'o' add 'es' to make the plural.

10) **airmen** — 'airman' becomes 'airmen'. This is an irregular plural.

11) **sheep** — 'sheep' does not change. This is an irregular plural.

12) **moose** — 'moose' does not change. This is an irregular plural.

13) **series** — 'series' does not change. This is an irregular plural.

14) **these** — 'this' becomes 'these'. This is an irregular plural.

15) **people** — 'person' becomes 'people'. This is an irregular plural.

16) **those** — 'that' becomes 'those'. This is an irregular plural.

17) **geese** — 'goose' becomes 'geese'. This is an irregular plural.

18) **mice** — 'mouse' becomes 'mice'. This is an irregular plural.

Page 15 — Homophones

1) **peek** — 'peek' makes sense here. It means 'to look briefly', whereas 'peak' is the top of something.

2) **dye** — 'dye' makes sense here. It means 'a colouring substance', whereas 'die' means 'to become dead'.

3) **buoy** — 'buoy' makes sense here. It is a float to moor boats to, whereas a 'boy' is a male child.

4) **owed** — 'owed' makes sense here. It means 'to have to pay or repay', whereas an 'ode' is a type of poem.

5) **reel** — 'reel' makes sense here. It is a cylinder that something is wound around, whereas 'real' means 'genuine'.

6) **gait** — 'gait' makes sense here. It means 'a way of walking', whereas a 'gate' is an entry to an enclosed space.

7) **gnaw** — 'gnaw' makes sense here. It means 'to chew', whereas 'nor' is used to introduce a negative statement.

8) **spa** — 'spa' makes sense here. It is a place people go for relaxation and therapies, whereas 'spar' means 'a fight'.

9) **loch** — 'loch' makes sense here. It is a lake or body of salt water that is nearly surrounded by land, whereas a 'lock' means 'a mechanism used to fasten something.'

10) **sow** — 'sow' makes sense here. It means 'to plant seeds', whereas 'so' means 'therefore' and 'sew' means 'to join together with stitches'.

11) **seize** — 'seize' makes sense here. It means 'to take hold of', whereas 'sees' means 'perceives' and 'seas' are large bodies of salt water.

12) **they're** — 'they're' makes sense here. It is a shortened version of 'they are', whereas 'there' is a word used to refer to a particular place and 'their' means 'belonging to them'.

13) **pair** — 'pair' makes sense here. It refers to two of something, whereas 'pear' is a type of fruit and 'pare' means 'to cut off an outer layer'.

14) **yore** — 'yore' makes sense here. It means 'long ago', whereas 'your' means 'belonging to you' and 'you're' is a shortened form of 'you are'.

15) **vain** — 'vain' makes sense here. It means 'having a high opinion of yourself', whereas 'vein' is a type of blood vessel and 'vane' is an object that shows wind direction.

16) **pours** — 'pours' makes sense here. It means 'to dispense liquid', whereas 'paws' are an animal's feet and 'pause' means 'a temporary break or gap'.

17) **raise** — 'raise' makes sense here. It means 'to increase', whereas 'rays' are beams of light and 'raze' means 'to destroy'.

18) **fore** — 'fore' makes sense here. It means 'the front', whereas 'for' is a preposition and 'four' is a number.

Page 16 — Prefixes and Suffixes

1) **in** — The word is 'intense'.

2) **pre** — The word is 'predate'.

3) **un** — The word is 'uneventful'.

4) **re** — The word is 'rearrange'.

5) **mis** — The word is 'misheard'.

6) **dis** — The word is 'dissimilar'.

7) **mis** — The word is 'mistakes'.

8) **in** — The word is 'inadequate'.

9) **re** — The word is 'regain'.

10) **speechless** — The suffix added is 'less'.

11) **movement** — The suffix added is 'ment'.

12) **preventable** — The suffix added is 'able'.

13) **invitation** — The suffix added is 'ation', but you also need to remove the 'e' from 'invite'.

14) **heaviness** — The suffix added is 'ness', but you also need to change the 'y' in 'heavy' to an 'i'.

15) **malicious** — The suffix added is 'ious', but you also need to remove the 'e' from 'malice'.

16) **persistence** — The suffix added is 'ence'.

17) **cheekily** — The suffix added is 'ly', but you also need to change the 'y' in 'cheeky' to an 'i'.

18) **complimentary** — The suffix added is 'ary'.

Page 17 — Awkward Spellings

1) **patient** — The vowel sound is spelt 'ie'.

2) **unveiled** — The vowel sound is spelt 'ei'.

3) **weigh** — The vowel sound is spelt 'ei'.

4) **deceitful** — It follows this rule: 'i before e except after c, but only when the vowel sound rhymes with bee'.

5) **efficiency** — The vowel sound is spelt 'ie'.

6) **achieve** — It follows this rule: 'i before e except after c, but only when the vowel sound rhymes with bee'.

7) **conceive** — It follows this rule: 'i before e except after c, but only when the vowel sound rhymes with bee'.

8) **receipt** — It follows this rule: 'i before e except after c, but only when the vowel sound rhymes with bee'.

9) **grievances** — It follows this rule: 'i before e except after c, but only when the vowel sound rhymes with bee'.

10) **ch tt** — The sentence is 'Hardi came up with a scheme to increase lettuce production on the allotment.'

11) **pp kn** — The sentence is 'I happen to have hurt my knuckle, so I can't hold a pen.'

12) **ll rh** — The sentence is 'The word had too many syllables, so it ruined the rhythm of my poem.'

13) **pp mm** — The sentence is 'Jaz was appointed as the group leader for their climb to the summit.'

14) **wr ll** — The sentence is 'Pia wrinkled her nose when she saw how polluted the water was.'

15) **tt mb** — The sentence is 'They said the lemon tart was bitter, but they only left crumbs on the plate.'

16) **rr gn** — The sentence is 'That year, William had arranged to visit three foreign countries on holiday.'

17) **wr ff** — The sentence is 'It was always a wrench leaving the farm, but this time felt different.'

18) **cc mb** — The sentence is 'Olly had an occasional ache in his arm, but mostly it felt numb.'

Page 18 — Mixed Spelling Questions

1) **lie** — 'lie' makes sense here because it means 'to get into a horizontal position'.

2) **lay** — 'lay' makes sense here because it means 'to put something down'.

3) **effect** — 'effect' makes sense here because it is a noun in the sentence.

4) **affect** — 'affect' makes sense here because it is a verb in the sentence.

5) **insure** — 'insure' makes sense here because it means 'to take out insurance'.

6) **ensure** — 'ensure' makes sense here because it means 'to make certain'.

7) **formally** — 'formally' makes sense here because it means 'in a correct and conventional way'.

8) **formerly** — 'formerly' makes sense here because it means 'in the past'.

9) **edition** — 'edition' makes sense here because it means 'a particular version of something'.

10) **addition** — 'addition' makes sense here because it means 'the action of adding'.

11) **humorous** — 'humourous' should be 'humorous'. When the suffix 'ous' is added to 'humour', you need to take away the 'u' before the 'r'.

12) **apparent** — 'apparant' should be 'apparent'. It ends in 'ent'.

13) **occasion** — 'ocasion' should be 'occasion'. It has a double 'c'.

14) **miniature** — 'minature' should be 'miniature'. There is a silent 'i'.

15) **grateful** — 'greatful' should be 'grateful'. 'grate' and 'great' are homophones.

16) **licence** — 'lisence' should be 'licence'. It has a 'c', not an 's'.

17) **accidentally** — 'accidentaly' should be 'accidentally'. The suffix 'ly' is added to 'accidental', so it has a double 'l'.

18) **experience** — 'experiance' should be 'experience'. It ends in 'ence'.

Section Four — Writers' Techniques

Page 19 — Alliteration and Onomatopoeia

1) **mouse marvelled massive mountain made**
The 'm' sound is used to form the alliteration.

2) **Herbert had how help Harriet's homework**
The 'h' sound is used to form the alliteration. 'honestly' is not part of the alliteration because the 'h' is silent.

3) **Kathy couldn't count considerable kangaroos**
The 'c' sound is used to form the alliteration. 'Kathy' and 'kangaroos' have a 'c' sound at the beginning so they are part of the alliteration.

4) **Walter Wilma while was**
The 'w' sound is used to form the alliteration. 'wrapped' is not part of the alliteration because the 'w' is silent.

5) **Surprisingly sweet sold century**
The 's' sound is used to form the alliteration. 'century' has an 's' sound at the beginning so it is part of the alliteration.

6) **party plenty people Polly**
The 'p' sound is used to form the alliteration. 'photograph' is not part of the alliteration because it starts with a softer 'ph' sound.

7) **chef shriek Charlotte shrimp**
The 'sh' sound is used to form the alliteration. 'chef' and 'Charlotte' have a 'sh' sound at the beginning so they are part of the alliteration.

8) **June Julia jungle gemstones**
The 'j' sound is used to form the alliteration. 'gemstones' has a 'j' sound at the beginning so it is part of the alliteration.

9) **known gnats never near**
The 'n' sound is used to form the alliteration. 'known' and 'gnats' have a 'n' sound at the beginning so they are part of the alliteration.

10) **gurgled** — 'gurgled' sounds like the noise a baby makes when it is happy.

11) **gushing** — 'gushing' sounds like the noise that water makes when it flows quickly.

12) **howling** — 'howling' sounds like the noise a wolf makes when it calls to other wolves.

13) **fluttered** — 'fluttered' sounds like the noise a butterfly's wings make as it flies.

14) **thudded** — 'thudded' sounds like the noise a bowling ball makes when it lands on the floor.

15) **clink** — 'clink' sounds like the noise that glasses make when they are knocked against each other.

16) **sloshing** — 'sloshing' sounds like the noise that soup makes when it moves around in a container.

17) **pattering** — 'pattering' sounds like the noise that raindrops make when they land on something.

18) **murmurs** — 'murmurs' sounds like the noise that somebody makes when they are talking softly.

Page 20 — Imagery

1) **metaphor** — This is a metaphor because the lake is described as being a mirror.

2) **personification** — This is personification because the kettle 'wailed' like a person.

3) **simile** — This is a simile because the teacher is being compared to a crocodile.

4) **metaphor** — This is a metaphor because Amelie is described as being a lighthouse.

5) **metaphor** — This is a metaphor because the dog is described as being a vacuum cleaner.

6) **simile** — This is a simile because Nora is being compared to a lion.

7) **simile** — This is a simile because Lucas's gentle stroking is being compared to waves lapping the shore.

8) **personification** — This is personification because the clouds 'threatened' the village like a person.

9) **personification** — This is personification because the leaves 'danced' like a person.

10) **many answers possible** — e.g. 'a roaring dragon'

11) **many answers possible** — e.g. 'giant watching me'

12) **many answers possible** — e.g. 'slithering snake'

13) **many answers possible** — e.g. 'boulder weighing her down'

14) **many answers possible** — e.g. 'a swan gliding across water'

15) **many answers possible** — e.g. 'magic spell cast over us'

16) **many answers possible** — e.g. 'the inside of an oven'

17) **many answers possible** — e.g. 'sprinting cheetah'

18) **many answers possible** — e.g. 'a dog getting a treat'

Page 21 — Abbreviations

1) **December** — 'Dec' is an abbreviation for 'December'.

2) **Doctor** — 'Dr' is an abbreviation for 'Doctor'.

3) **kilograms** — 'kg' is an abbreviation for 'kilograms'.

4) **minimum** — 'min' is an abbreviation for 'minimum'.

5) **Captain** — 'Capt' is an abbreviation for 'Captain'.

6) **appointment** — 'appt' is an abbreviation for 'appointment'.

7) **Tuesday** — 'Tues' is an abbreviation for 'Tuesday'.

8) **weeks** — 'wks' is an abbreviation for 'weeks'.

9) **Government** — 'Govt' is an abbreviation for 'Government'.

10) **acronym** — 'ASAP' is the acronym for 'as soon as possible'.

11) **abbreviation** — 'Pres' is an abbreviation for 'President'.

12) **acronym** — 'DOB' is the acronym for 'date of birth'.

13) **acronym** — 'DAB' is the acronym for 'digital audio broadcasting'.

14) **abbreviation** — 'Lang' is an abbreviation for 'language'.

15) **acronym** — 'DIY' is the acronym for 'do it yourself'.

16) **abbreviation** — 'lb' is an abbreviation for 'pounds'.

17) **abbreviation** — 'No.' is an abbreviation for 'number'.

18) **acronym**— 'VIP' is the acronym for 'very important person'.

Page 22 — Synonyms and Antonyms

1) **irked** — 'irritated' and 'irked' both mean 'annoyed'.

2) **irresponsible** — 'reckless' and 'irresponsible' both mean 'careless'.

3) **predicted** — 'anticipated' and 'predicted' both mean 'expected'.

4) **misleading** — 'deceptive' and 'misleading' both mean 'causing someone to believe something that is wrong'.

5) **gracefully** — 'elegantly' and 'gracefully' both mean 'moving in a smooth and graceful way'.

6) **curious** — 'inquisitive' and 'curious' both mean 'questioning'.

7) **hostile** — 'aggressive' and 'hostile' both mean 'unfriendly'.

8) **interpret** — 'decipher' and 'interpret' both mean 'to work out the meaning of'.

9) **perceived** — 'noticed' and 'perceived' both mean 'became aware'.

10) **dated** — 'modern' means 'up to date' whereas 'dated' means 'old-fashioned'.

11) **permitted** — 'forbidden' means 'not allowed' whereas 'permitted' means 'allowed'.

12) **eager** — 'hesitant' means 'reluctant' whereas 'eager' means 'keen'.

13) **delighted** — 'repulsed' means 'disgusted' whereas 'delighted' means 'pleased'.

14) **shortened** — 'extended' means 'made longer' whereas 'shortened' means 'made shorter'.

15) **minuscule** — 'immense' means 'very large' whereas 'minuscule' means 'tiny'.

16) **chaotic** — 'tranquil' means 'peaceful' whereas 'chaotic' means 'frenzied'.

17) **appeased** — 'angered' means 'caused upset' whereas 'appeased' means 'calmed'.

18) **despised** — 'treasured' means 'adored' whereas 'despised' means 'hated'.

Page 23 — Spotting and Understanding Devices

1) **simile** — This is a simile because Amani's classmates are compared to seagulls.

2) **abbreviation** — 'p' is an abbreviation for 'pence'.

3) **personification** — This is personification because the cake 'grinned' like a person.

4) **onomatopoeia** — This is an example of onomatopoeia because 'chomped' sounds like the noise a person makes when they take a bite of something.

5) **alliteration** — The 'd' sound is repeated at the beginning of 'demanding', 'delicious' and 'delicacies'.

6) **A** — This comparison to the ocean suggests that the crowd is moving — the word 'rolling' implies that the people are rising up and down like waves.

7) **B** — The word 'gulped' suggests that Amani is nervous, as swallowing loudly is something a person typically does when they are feeling anxious.

Page 24 — Spotting and Understanding Devices

1) **a room as silent as a graveyard** — 'a room as silent as a graveyard' is a simile because the silence of the room is being compared to the silence of a graveyard.

2) **a bird alighting on a branch** — This is a metaphor because it is describing the child as being a bird landing on a branch.

3) **E.g. the boxes they opened only coughing up dust** — This is personification because the boxes were 'coughing' like a person.

4) **warily** — 'timidly' and 'warily' both mean 'cautiously'.

5) **peculiar** — 'ordinary' means 'normal', whereas 'peculiar' means 'odd'.

6) **B** — The word 'heave' suggests the person is putting a lot of effort into moving something.

7) **C** — The word 'ominously' gives the impression that the stairs made a threatening sound, which creates tension.

Section Five — Writing

Page 25 — Writing Fiction

There are many possible answers to the questions on this page. We've put some ideas below to help.

1) **e.g.** Saffy raised her hand, desperate for the teacher to choose her.

2) **e.g.** Mud-spattered after winning his match, Ali sauntered down the road.

3) **e.g.** Hearing a whirring noise above her head, the girl looked up.

4) **e.g.** He picked up the pen and started writing feverishly before the dream disappeared.

5) **e.g.** Zaki shook his head as Mark carried on revealing their secret plan.

6) **e.g.** Despite trying to contain her merriment, Helena laughed out loud.

7) **e.g.** The crowd drifted away as soon as the spectacle was over.

8) **e.g.** Miles cheered loudly and clapped his hands in delight.

9) **e.g.** With no idea what would happen, he pulled on the rope.

10) **e.g.** 'disused' and 'murky'.

11) **e.g.** 'headstrong' and 'dazzling'.

12) **e.g.** 'gleaming' and 'gnarled'.

13) **e.g.** 'elderly' and 'sunlit'.

14) **e.g.** 'contented' and 'well-thumbed'.

15) **e.g.** 'jaunty' and 'bearded'.

16) **e.g.** 'crooked' and 'dank'.

17) **e.g.** 'fragrant' and 'industrious'.

18) **e.g.** 'narrow' and 'panelled'.

Page 26 — Writing Fiction

There are many possible answers to the questions on this page. We've put some ideas below to help.

1) **e.g.** 'hushed' and 'dusty'
'Dusty books lined the walls, absorbing noise and adding to the hushed atmosphere.'

2) **e.g.** 'kind' and 'friendly'
'The kind nurse gave a friendly wave as I left the ward.'

3) **e.g.** 'bustling' and 'rowdy'
'The rowdy cries mingled with comings and goings in the bustling hall.'

4) **e.g.** 'salt-laden' and 'golden'
'The salt-laden gusts lifted the golden sand into hazy swirls.'

5) **e.g.** 'skilled' and 'powerful'
'The skilled diver gave a powerful thrust of her legs, propelling her downwards.'

6) **e.g.** 'curious' and 'shaggy'
'The shaggy dog gave a curious sniff as the scent of a barbecue wafted by.'

7) **many answers possible** — Make sure you plan the beginning, middle and end of your story and then stick to your plan when you are writing.

8) **many answers possible** — Make sure you plan the beginning, middle and end of your story and then stick to your plan when you are writing.

9) **many answers possible** — Make sure you plan the beginning, middle and end of your story and then stick to your plan when you are writing.

10) **many answers possible** — Make sure you plan the beginning, middle and end of your story and then stick to your plan when you are writing.

11) **many answers possible** — Make sure you plan the beginning, middle and end of your story and then stick to your plan when you are writing.

Page 27 — Writing Non-Fiction

1) **D** — This sentence is describing a scene.

2) **I** — This sentence is informing the reader about badgers.

3) **D** — This sentence is describing the boy.

4) **P** — This sentence is persuading the reader to join a march.

5) **I** — This sentence is informing the reader about fizzy drinks.

6) **P** — This sentence is persuading the reader that cats are better than dogs.

7) **I** — This sentence is informing the reader about Earth's atmosphere.

8) **many answers possible** — Coming up with points that form a clear argument before you start writing will help you write a structured answer in the test.

9) **many answers possible** — Coming up with points that form a clear argument before you start writing will help you write a structured answer in the test.

Page 28 — Writing Non-Fiction

There are many possible answers to the questions on this page. We've put some ideas below to help.

1) **e.g.** — For: You're more likely to improve your skills in a sport if it's the only one you play. Against: You miss out on other sports you may be good at and enjoy.

2) **e.g.** — For: It's a good way for children to learn how to be independent. Against: Children are already busy with school, homework, hobbies and friends.

3) **e.g.** — For: With shorter holidays, there would be time to learn subjects in more depth. Against: Children need a proper break to relax and pursue other interests.

4) **e.g.** — For: It is easy to waste time on social media, so limiting access would help avoid this. Against: Children may have friends and family who live far away, and limiting social media use would restrict contact with them.

5) **e.g.** — For: It would let students gain a deeper knowledge of subjects they enjoy and are interested in. Against: It could mean students miss out on important knowledge in other areas.

6) **many answers possible** — Make sure you plan an introduction, at least three middle points and a conclusion, and then stick to your plan when you are writing.

7) **many answers possible** — Make sure you plan an introduction, at least three middle points and a conclusion, and then stick to your plan when you are writing.

8) **many answers possible** — Make sure you plan an introduction, at least three middle points and a conclusion, and then stick to your plan when you are writing.

9) **many answers possible** — Make sure you plan an introduction, at least three middle points and a conclusion, and then stick to your plan when you are writing.

10) **many answers possible** — Make sure you plan an introduction, at least three middle points and a conclusion, and then stick to your plan when you are writing.

Assessment Tests

Pages 29-36 — Assessment Test 1

1) **D** — In the passage it says Gil "grumbled", which shows that he is annoyed at Rab for not being as much fun as he used to be.

2) **C** — The passage mentions "newly harvested fields" but there is no mention of the type of crop grown.

3) **B** — Gil tries "to coax a smile" from Rab, so he wants to cheer him up and make him feel better.

4) **D** — The passage says that Rab missed the "game of soldiers" he used to play after school with his friends who lived "nearby".

5) **D** — In the passage the farm is described as being on a "hilltop" and in winter it doesn't keep out the "cold and damp", so it faces difficult weather conditions.

6) **A** — The passage tells us that their father borrowed money from their landlord.

7) **E** — The text mentions how the land was "sucking the life from them" but it does not mention not having enough food to eat as a reason for this.

8) **A** — The passage says that the view "was enough to lift Rab's spirits", which shows he feels grateful for the sight.

9) **E** — "huddled" is closest in meaning to 'grouped together'.

10) **C** — "admit" is closest in meaning to 'accept'.

11) **A** — In this sentence the word "toiled" could most accurately be replaced by 'laboured'. It means 'to work hard'.

12) **D** — "wearily" is an adverb. It describes the verb "sighed".

13) **E** — This is a simile because the author is saying that the geese look like sailboats.

14) **B** — Smiling is something that people do, so this is an example of personification because the heavens are described as 'doing' a human action.

15) **C** — In the passage it says that Holi is "observed in many countries by Hindus and non-Hindus alike".

16) **B** — The passage tells us that the Demon King "demanded people treat him" like a god, so he should be worshipped in place of other gods.

17) **A** — In the passage it says that Prahlad "prayed to Vishnu for protection" and that Vishnu had a "victorious rescue of Prahlad".

18) **D** — In the passage it says that Holika was "immune to fire", so the Demon King most likely assumed that she wouldn't be harmed by the flames.

19) **E** — The passage tells us that Holika "perished in the blaze", which means that she died.

20) **D** — Rangwali Holi is full of "colourful chaos" and people "rejoice" in the festivities. This suggests the festival is bustling and lively.

21) **E** — Holi is "observed in many countries" but the exact number of people who celebrate it is not mentioned.

22) **B** — The passage tells us that "Hindus consider Holi to signify the triumph of good over evil".

23) **E** — "victorious" is closest in meaning to 'successful'.

24) **C** — "congregate" is closest in meaning to 'gather'. It means 'to come together and form a group'.

25) **D** — "in" is a preposition. It shows where Holika was in relation to the blaze.

26) **B** — These are adjectives because they describe nouns.

27) **C** — Metaphors describe something as being something else. This is a metaphor because the people are being described as rainbows.

28) **B** — Rejoicing is something that people do, so it is personification because the cities and towns are described as 'doing' a human action.

29) **D** — 'apetites' should be 'appetites' — it needs a double 'p'.

30) **C** — 'seller' should be 'cellar'. The words are homophones — a 'seller' is someone who sells things whereas a 'cellar' is an underground room beneath a building.

31) **N** — There are no mistakes in this line.

32) **B** — 'flatterring' should be 'flattering'. The 'r' should not be doubled when the suffix 'ing' is added.

33) **C** — 'referance' should be 'reference'. The suffix is 'ence' not 'ance'.

34) **A** — 'anxeity' should be 'anxiety'. The vowel sound is spelt 'ie'.

35) **C** — 'under' is the only preposition which makes sense here.

36) **E** — 'had' completes the verb phrase 'had been watching', and matches the tense of the rest of the passage, which is in the past tense.

37) **A** — 'when' is the only word which makes sense here.

38) **B** — 'been' completes the verb phrase 'had been cancelled'.

39) **C** — 'that' is the only option which makes sense here.

40) **B** — 'few' is the only adjective that makes sense here.

41) **D** — There should be a full stop after 'computers' because it is the end of a sentence.

42) **B** — There should be a comma between 'tombola' and 'there' because 'As well as the usual raffle and tombola' is a subordinate clause.

43) **C** — There should be a colon between 'ways' and 'donating' to introduce a list.

44) **B** — 'Its' should be 'It's' because it is short for 'It is'.

45) C — There should be a comma between 'Adams' and 'told' because commas are needed at the start and end of the extra information, 'Mrs Adams'.

46) N — There are no mistakes in this line.

47) C — There should be a set of inverted commas before the word 'I'm' to introduce the speech.

48) A — 'poster's' should be 'posters' — the 's' shows that the noun is plural. It doesn't show possession so it doesn't need an apostrophe.

49) N — There are no mistakes in this line.

50) D — 'Summer' is a common noun so it doesn't need a capital letter.

Pages 37-44 — Assessment Test 2

1) B — The passage tells us that Esperanza's father "never disappointed her", which suggests that he is reliable.

2) B — In the passage it says that Esperanza's father "had promised to meet her in the garden", which suggests that she is in the garden because she is waiting for him.

3) D — The passage tells us that Esperanza's father "brought beef jerky" home "Sometimes", which suggests that the gift of beef jerky isn't specifically related to Esperanza's birthday.

4) C — The passage tells us that Esperanza's father is "always home before sundown", so she is worried because it is getting dark and he has not returned.

5) D — The passage tells us that the flower that pricked Esperanza was "fully opened", which means it has bloomed.

6) A — The passage tells us he always comes home "dusty from the mesquite grasslands." This suggests he works outside in the grasslands.

7) B — In the passage it says that Esperanza keeps the linens made by her mother "for someday".

8) D — The passage tells us that Esperanza has received a doll "every year since she was born", but it doesn't mention how many dolls Esperanza has or how old she is.

9) B — "nagged at" is closest in meaning to 'bothered'.

10) D — "dismissed" is closest in meaning to 'rejected'.

11) C — "premonition" means 'feeling'.

12) A — "embroidered" means 'decorated'.

13) D — "into" is a preposition because it tells you where the linens are in relation to the trunk.

14) E — This is an adverb because it describes the verb "thought".

15) B — In the passage, it says that Holly is "intrigued" about where Alfie goes at night.

16) B — The camera is described as "compact" which means 'small'.

17) C — In the passage, it says that Holly has "always" been interested in where Alfie goes at night, and now she has a chance to find out the answer.

18) A — In Holly's imagination, Alfie is compared to "an intrepid explorer" which makes him sound brave and adventurous.

19) D — The door is described as "ajar" which means 'slightly open'.

20) D — In the passage, the supermarket workers tickle Alfie in his "favourite spot" which suggests they know him, and he lets them rub his tummy which he only lets certain people do.

21) E — In the passage, it says that Holly has to wait "a couple of nights in vain" before she can capture any footage, which suggests that Alfie doesn't go outside every night.

22) A — The supermarket is described as being "24-hour" which means that it's open all the time.

23) E — "smudges" is closest in meaning to the word 'smears', as they both mean 'a blurred, messy mark'.

24) A — "luxurious" is closest in meaning to the word 'indulgent' — they both mean 'comfortable'.

25) B — "skirting" can most accurately be replaced by 'going around the edge of'.

26) C — "was" is the verb because it describes the action in the sentence.

27) D — "twisted" is an adjective because it describes a noun, "branches".

28) B — "thump" is an example of onomatopoeia because the word makes the sound of a cat flap banging against the door.

29) A — 'into' is the only preposition which makes sense here.

30) B — 'from' is the only preposition which makes sense here.

31) E — 'rustle' is the only option which makes sense here.

32) B — 'saw' completes the phrase 'widened when she saw', which is in the past tense.

33) E — 'were' is the only option which makes sense here.

34) C — 'going' matches the tense of the rest of the sentence.

35) B — Inverted commas are needed after 'everybody!' because it is the end of Mum's speech.

36) A — There shouldn't be an opening bracket before 'the aquarium'. The brackets should only be around 'my favourite place ever' because this is the extra information.

37) C — There should be a colon between 'see' and 'an' to introduce the list.

38) N — There are no mistakes in this line.

39) B — 'scale's' should be 'scales' — the 's' shows that the noun is plural. It doesn't show possession so it doesn't need an apostrophe.

40) A — 'its' should be 'it's' — 'it's' is the shortened version of 'it is' so it needs an apostrophe.

41) C — 'joyusly' should be 'joyously'. The suffixes 'ous' and 'ly' are added to the root word 'joy' to form the adverb 'joyously'.

42) C — 'legendry' should be 'legendary'. The suffix is 'ary'.

43) N — There are no mistakes in this line.

44) **D** — 'pail' should be 'pale'. The words are homophones — 'pail' is another word for 'bucket' whereas 'pale' means 'lacking colour'.

45) **A** — 'wimper' should be 'whimper'. The 'h' in 'whimper' is a silent letter.

46) **C** — 'prosessed' should be 'processed'. The 'c' in processed makes an 's' sound.

47) **C** — 'sufficiant' should be 'sufficient'. The suffix is 'ent' not 'ant'.

48) **D** — 'remarkible' should be 'remarkable'. The suffix is 'able' not 'ible'.

49) **A** — 'oppurtunity' should be 'opportunity' — the unstressed vowel is 'o'.

50) **C** — 'ashured' should be 'assured'. It needs a double 's'.

Pages 45-52 — Assessment Test 3

1) **B** — The writer says that TV "can be informative and entertaining".

2) **D** — The writer gives the overall amount of time young people spend looking at screens, but not how much of this time is spent on phones.

3) **A** — The writer mentions hiking, swimming, cycling and climbing trees, but not climbing mountains.

4) **C** — The writer describes navigating a route as an "achievement".

5) **D** — The text mentions "moor", "mountain", "forest" and "shore", but not grassland.

6) **C** — The questions are intended to make the reader think about whether skills and knowledge of the outdoors are better gained first-hand.

7) **B** — The writer says that spending time outside "doesn't only benefit the body", meaning it's healthy, and lists some of the stimulating activities people can do outdoors.

8) **E** — The passage is biased, as it argues strongly that people should spend more time outside.

9) **B** — This is an idiom that means 'To make matters worse'.

10) **A** — "forgoing" is closest in meaning to 'doing without'.

11) **E** — The word "profound" could most accurately be replaced by 'deep'.

12) **B** — "squander" means 'waste'.

13) **D** — This is personification because the breeze is described as giving a "caress" or stroke, like a person might.

14) **D** — "guarantee" is a verb in this context. It means 'promise'.

15) **C** — The line "Searching my heart for its true sorrow", along with the longing tone of the first two verses, suggests the narrator feels 'wistful'.

16) **D** — The narrator says "I am weary of words and people", which suggests they have grown tired of how busy the city is.

17) **C** — The poet describes "the loud sound and the soft sound" of the waves. This implies the sound of the sea doesn't stay the same.

18) **A** — The narrator describes how they "climbed the wave at morning" and "Shook the sand from my shoes at night". They later say they felt happy "All day long on the coast". These statements imply they would spend the whole day by the sea.

19) **E** — "wrecked", in this context, means 'shipwrecked' or 'beached on land', whilst "rotting" means 'decaying' or 'disintegrating', so the ships are 'damaged and disintegrating'.

20) **B** — The narrator describes "ships", "gulls", "mussels" and "spray" — they do not write about 'rocks'.

21) **C** — The narrator is "Sick of the city" and has been "too long away from water" — this implies they have been living in the city for a significant amount of time.

22) **A** — The narrator writes "I should be happy", but is "Never at all" since they came "here". The speaker is in the city in the present day, so this suggests they haven't been happy since they came to the city. They go on to say "I have a need of water near", which suggests they would be happier if they were by the sea.

23) **B** — This is an example of alliteration because the 's' sound is repeated at the beginning of "sticky", "salty" and "sweetness".

24) **D** — "fence" is a verb in this context — it means 'to surround something'.

25) **D** — "Stricken" is closest in meaning to 'deeply affected'. It means to be overwhelmed by something painful or difficult.

26) **E** — This is personification because the piles are "groaning" like a person.

27) **C** — "wheeling" means 'flying in a circle' in this context.

28) **A** — "Maine" is a proper noun — it is the name of a US state.

29) **A** — There should be a comma between 'Archery' and 'the' to separate the extra information — 'the use of a bow and arrow to hit a target'.

30) **D** — There should be a semicolon between 'animals' and 'as'. This is to separate the items in the list.

31) **N** — There are no mistakes in this line.

32) **D** — There shouldn't be a hyphen joining 'metres' and 'away'.

33) **B** — 'its' should be 'it's' — 'it's' is the shortened version of 'it is' so it needs an apostrophe.

34) **D** — There should be a full stop after 'off course' to mark the end of the sentence.

35) **N** — There are no mistakes in this line.

36) **C** — 'faithfull' should be 'faithful'. The suffix 'ful' doesn't have a double 'l'.

37) **C** — 'agressive' should be 'aggressive' — it needs a double 'g'.

38) **A** — 'qualitys' should be 'qualities' — if the letter before the 'y' is a consonant then you remove the 'y' and add 'ies' to make it plural.

39) **B** — 'affectian' should be 'affection'. The suffix is 'ion'.

40) **A** — 'doutting' should be 'doubting'. There should be a silent 'b' instead of the first 't'.

41) **D** — 'to' is the only word which makes sense here.

42) **D** — 'sneak' matches the tense of the rest of the sentence.

43) **E** — 'had' completes the verb phrase 'had stolen' and agrees with the subject, 'the thieves'.

44) **A** — 'Preparing' is the only option which makes sense here.

45) **B** — 'while' is the only word which makes sense here.

46) **C** — 'had made' matches the tense of the sentence, which is in the past tense, and agrees with Elna, which is singular.

47) **A** — 'during' is the only preposition that makes sense here.

48) **C** — 'were' is the only option that makes sense here.

49) **C** — 'Before' is the only word that makes sense here.

50) **A** — 'focused' matches the tense of the start of the sentence, which is in the past tense.

Pages 53-60 — Assessment Test 4

1) **A** — In the passage, the window is described as "grimy".

2) **D** — Adam's notepad is "battered" and "smudged" because it has been used a lot. His pencil is "well-chewed" because he has spent a lot of time chewing his pencil whilst drawing.

3) **C** — In the passage it says Adam is "trying to capture the sunlight in his drawing" before throwing his pencil "in frustration".

4) **A** — In the passage it says "Adam was more interested in Icarus *before* the fall". Adam draws Icarus preparing to fly, suggesting that this is what interests him about Icarus before the fall.

5) **B** — In the passage Adam draws Daedalus as a "blurry shape".

6) **B** — Daedalus is worried about Icarus — he shows his concern by asking and warning his son not to fly too near to the sun.

7) **B** — In this context, "furiously" means 'energetically'. Adam is drawing energetically because he feels inspired after he remembers the painting shown to him by his art teacher.

8) **D** — In the passage it says Adam would go to the attic room "to leave the shadows of the day behind". In this context, the "shadows of the day" means the difficult moments from the day. So when he is in the attic room he feels 'safe and unburdened'.

9) **D** — "plunged" is closest in meaning to 'fell'.

10) **D** — In this sentence the word "unfurled" could most accurately be replaced by 'open'.

11) **A** — "strewn" is closest in meaning to 'scattered'.

12) **C** — "who" is an example of a pronoun.

13) **E** — These words are examples of prepositions.

14) **C** — "*The sun gives us life*" is an example of a statement.

15) **B** — In the passage it says that "their lives would be at risk" without the sun's warmth.

16) **C** — The passage tells us that Coyote "whimpered" when he heard the humans worrying about winter and that he was "Determined to be of assistance" to them.

17) **D** — In the passage it says that the Fire Spirits "would not share their fire willingly".

18) **E** — In the passage it says that when Coyote meets the humans, their faces "lit up with hope", which suggests that they were happy to see him.

19) **C** — The passage tells us that the fire was left unguarded "every morning", which shows that the Fire Spirits' routine was predictable.

20) **A** — In the passage it says that when the Fire Spirits first saw Coyote, they "paid him no mind". This suggests they weren't interested in him, so they were 'indifferent'.

21) **B** — The passage tells us that the Fire Spirits "knew of no way to coax fire out of wood", so they left.

22) **C** — The passage tells us that Coyote "went to the mountains" but it doesn't say how far away the mountains are.

23) **B** — "malicious" is closest in meaning to 'evil'.

24) **E** — "abundance" means 'large supply'.

25) **D** — "coax" is closest in meaning to 'persuade'.

26) **E** — This is an adverb because it describes the verb "studied".

27) **D** — This is an example of alliteration because the 's' sound is repeated.

28) **C** — This is a simile because the author is saying that fear is like ice.

29) **C** — 'independant' should be 'independent'. The suffix is 'ent' not 'ant'.

30) **D** — 'assistence' should be 'assistance'. The suffix is 'ance' not 'ence'.

31) **B** — 'asert' should be 'assert' — it needs a double 's'.

32) **C** — 'furnature' should be 'furniture'.

33) **N** — There are no mistakes in this line.

34) **B** — 'piece' should be 'peace'. The words are homophones — 'piece' is a part of something, whereas 'peace' means 'calm'.

35) **D** — 'near' is the only preposition which makes sense here.

36) **A** — 'visited' completes the verb phrase 'are visited'.

37) **B** — 'lit' is the only option which makes sense here.

38) **C** — 'along' is the only preposition which makes sense here.

39) **D** — 'Additionally' is the only conjunction which makes sense here because it introduces the extra activity that people can do in the caves.

40) **B** — 'listen' completes the verb phrase 'they can also listen', and matches the tense of the sentence, which is in the present tense.

41) **N** — There are no mistakes in this line.

42) **B** — There should be a comma between 'spoke' and 'sang' to separate the items in the list.

43) **C** — Inverted commas are needed after 'relax,' because it is the end of Mr Ellison's speech.

44) **A** — There should be a hyphen joining 'jam' and 'packed' to make it clear that Declan's brain is full.

45) **B** — 'but' should be 'But' because the word is at the start of a sentence.

46) **A** — There should be a dash between 'stage' and 'only' to separate the extra information.

47) **C** — There should be a question mark after 'something' because the sentence in inverted commas is a question.

48) **C** — There should be a comma between 'calm' and 'wasn't'. This is to separate the extra information — 'which was now quiet and calm'.

49) **A** — 'Declans' should be 'Declan's'. The possessive apostrophe goes before the 's' because there is only one Declan.

50) **D** — 'hed' should be 'he'd'. 'he'd' is a shortened version of 'he would' — the apostrophe represents the missing letters.

Pages 61-68 — Assessment Test 5

1) **B** — In the passage it says that Violet and Alaric are trying to find "the herb that remedies all ills".

2) **E** — In the passage it says that "once-harmless sounds" were "becoming ominous", but it doesn't say that Violet's hearing becomes better.

3) **E** — In the passage it says that "Alaric couldn't conceal the tremor in his voice", which suggests that he is scared.

4) **B** — Violet says that the sounds she hears in the tunnel could come from a demon, but there is no mention of her actually hearing a demon speak.

5) **C** — In the passage Alaric says that the king will "cease persecuting" witches if Violet finds the special herb. 'Persecuting' means to treat someone badly due to their identity.

6) **E** — In the passage it says that Violet was "Biting back her disbelief" at Alaric's words regarding the king's promises, which shows she doesn't trust them.

7) **A** — The passage says that Violet was walking at a "snail-like speed", which suggests their progress through the tunnels was slow.

8) **C** — The passage tells us that Violet feared "losing all sense of direction entirely" when the wall disappeared.

9) **B** — "stifle" is closest in meaning to 'suppress'.

10) **D** — "salvage" means 'save'.

11) **E** — This is an adjective because it describes the air.

12) **C** — These are verbs because they are action words.

13) **B** — This contains an example of onomatopoeia because "shuffled" sounds like the noise people's shoes make when they walk.

14) **E** — This is personification because the gloom behaved like a human when it "taunted" Violet and Alaric.

15) **E** — The narrator's name isn't mentioned in the passage.

16) **D** — In the passage it says "the sky was bluest of the blue" and the pools "flashed the colour back". This means the pools appeared blue.

17) **C** — In the passage the narrator says "there was no stopping for me" when they first heard their name being called.

18) **E** — Charlotte's voice is described as "plaintive", which means 'sorrowful'.

19) **A** — In the passage it says that they didn't need to talk because the "glory of existing on this perfect morning" was enough to satisfy them.

20) **B** — The narrator says "It was a strange craze" but "there were points about the game", which suggests they saw its appeal although it was unusual.

21) **A** — In the passage it says that Harold "always stuck staunchly to a new fad", which means he was committed to it.

22) **C** — The passage describes a "sun-bathed world" and "wind-swept morning", so the day was 'Sunny and windy'.

23) **A** — "lurking" means 'hiding'.

24) **E** — "petulance" is closest in meaning to 'sulkiness'.

25) **D** — In this sentence the word "phantom" could most accurately be replaced by 'imaginary'.

26) **B** — "harmony" means 'agreement'.

27) **C** — "kindle" is a verb. It is the action word of the sentence.

28) **B** — "staircases" and "bell" are both nouns.

29) **C** — There should be a colon or a dash after 'spectacle' to introduce the new information — 'the annual hot air balloon festival'.

30) **C** — Inverted commas are needed after the question mark because it is the end of Kai's speech.

31) **A** — 'therell' should have an apostrophe before 'll' because it is a shortened version of two words, 'there' and 'will'.

32) **A** — The adjective 'faint' relates directly to the noun 'sound', so a hyphen isn't needed.

33) **N** — There are no mistakes in this line.

34) **A** — There should be a semicolon between 'lime' and 'a'. This is to separate the items in the list.

35) **C** — 'of' is the only word which makes sense here.

36) **D** — 'before' is the only word that makes sense here.

37) **B** — 'have' completes the verb phrase 'make sure you have', and matches the tense of the sentence, which is in the present tense.

38) **A** — 'filled' completes the verb phrase 'filled with hay'.

39) **D** — 'Although' is the only conjunction which makes sense here.

40) **C** — 'average' is the only word which makes sense here.

41) **B** — 'desided' should be 'decided' — the 'c' makes an 's' sound because it is followed by an 'i'.

42) **C** — 'rughly' should be 'roughly'.

43) **C** — 'explaning' should be 'explaining'.

44) **A** — 'predictians' should be 'predictions'. The suffix is 'ions' not 'ians'.

45) **N** — There are no mistakes in this line.

46) **C** — 'locacion' should be 'location'. The suffix is 'tion' not 'cion'.

47) **B** — 'cubboard' should be 'cupboard'. The 'p' in 'cupboard' is a silent letter.

48) **B** — 'rennovating' should be 'renovating' — it doesn't need a double 'n'.

49) **N** — There are no mistakes in this line.

50) **B** — 'suspence' should be 'suspense' — it ends in 'se' not 'ce'.

Pages 69-76 — Assessment Test 6

1) **E** — In the passage it says that books help readers with "their learning at school and beyond", but that "TV can also be educational".

2) **D** — The passage describes books as "traditional", whereas televisions are "state-of-the-art" with "crystal-clear images and immersive audio". This suggests that televisions have more features that engage the senses, so they seem more impressive.

3) **A** — In the passage it says that viewers can see "unfamiliar spectacles" on television.

4) **C** — The passage mentions television's "crystal-clear images and immersive audio", as well as its view into "a multitude of locations and cultures", but it doesn't mention how much of the screen the images fill.

5) **E** — The passage tells us that reading involves "engaging with the text to bring it to life", whereas viewers don't need to use their imaginations when they watch television, as they have "crystal-clear images" presented to them.

6) **C** — In the passage it says that there was a "monumental rise in the popularity of television", but it doesn't specify why.

7) **B** — The passage tells us that by reading, "readers' vocabularies also tend to improve", which helps with "their learning at school".

8) **E** — The passage tells us that both are "valuable in deepening our relationship with the world around us".

9) **D** — "staggering" is closest in meaning to 'astonishing'.

10) **E** — "witnessing" is closest in meaning to 'observing'.

11) **C** — "merits" is closest in meaning to 'benefits'.

12) **D** — These words are verbs because they are action words.

13) **C** — This line contains personification because the novel "could triumph" over television, like a person could win against somebody else.

14) **D** — The phrase 'expand your horizons' is an idiom that means 'to have new experiences'.

15) **D** — The narrator says that their "heart" feels "calm" as they watch the sunset.

16) **A** — The colour of the rivers is not mentioned.

17) **E** — The birds are flying "homeward", so they are flying back to their nests.

18) **B** — The bees are collecting food, as the previous line states the "wild fawns feed" on grasses, while the bees feed "on the cactus-gold".

19) **C** — The music comes from "a shepherd's pipe".

20) **C** — In the poem it says that the "fresh delights unfold" when "the bright shower passes". The "bright shower" is most likely rain, as it causes plants to grow.

21) **E** — The poet says that the stars "herald a rising moon". "herald" means 'announce'.

22) **D** — The young *Banjara* is singing a "ballad". A ballad is a song that tells a story.

23) **D** — "haven" is closest in meaning to 'refuge'.

24) **B** — "wistful" could most accurately be replaced by 'melancholy'.

25) **E** — The phrase 'lift up your voice' means 'start to sing'.

26) **A** — "whirl" is used as a noun in this sentence.

27) **C** — "gleam" is a verb. It is the action word in the sentence.

28) **E** — This is an example of alliteration because the 'fr' sound is repeated.

29) **N** — There are no mistakes in this line.

30) **A** — 'destinasion' should be 'destination'. The suffix is 'tion' not 'sion'.

31) **D** — 'monumants' should be 'monuments'. The ending is 'ents' not 'ants'.

32) **A** — 'Anually' should be 'Annually' — it has a double 'n'.

33) **A** — 'abundence' should be 'abundance'. The suffix is 'ance' not 'ence'.

34) **C** — 'you're' should be 'your' — 'you're' is a contraction of the words 'you' and 'are', which doesn't make sense here.

35) **B** — 'york' should be 'York' — it is a proper noun.

36) **N** — There are no mistakes in this line.

37) **C** — There should be a dash between the words 'artwork' and 'but'. The dashes separate the extra information.

38) **D** — There should be a comma after the word 'paintings' to separate the items in the list.

39) **A** — There shouldn't be an apostrophe in 'watercolour's'. The 's' has been added to make the word plural.

40) **C** — The writer is asking a question so there should be a question mark after 'here', not a full stop.

41) **C** — 'Last' is the only word which makes sense here.

42) **D** — 'followed' completes the verb phrase 'I followed a new recipe', and matches the tense of the rest of the passage, which is in the past tense.

43) **B** — 'in' is the only preposition which makes sense here.

44) **D** — 'would' is the only word which makes sense here.

45) **A** — 'Once' is the only conjunction which makes sense here.

46) **E** — 'with' is the only preposition which makes sense here.

47) **B** — 'After' is the only word which makes sense here.

48) **E** — 'make' completes the verb phrase 'to make it look'.

49) **C** — 'took' completes the verb phrase 'took several photographs', and matches the tense of the rest of the passage, which is in the past tense.

50) **A** — 'pleased' completes the verb phrase 'I was so pleased with', and matches the tense of the rest of the passage, which is in the past tense.

Progress Chart

Use this chart to keep track of your scores for the <u>Assessment Tests</u>.

You can do each test more than once — download extra answer sheets from <u>cgpbooks.co.uk/11plus/answer-sheets</u> or scan the QR code on the right.

Answer Sheets

	First Go	**Second Go**	**Third Go**
Test 1	Date: Score:	Date: Score:	Date: Score:
Test 2	Date: Score:	Date: Score:	Date: Score:
Test 3	Date: Score:	Date: Score:	Date: Score:
Test 4	Date: Score:	Date: Score:	Date: Score:
Test 5	Date: Score:	Date: Score:	Date: Score:
Test 6	Date: Score:	Date: Score:	Date: Score:

Look back at your scores once you've done all the <u>Assessment Tests</u>.
Each test is out of <u>50 marks</u>.

Work out which kind of mark you scored most often:

0-29 marks — Go back to <u>basics</u> and work on your <u>question technique</u>.

30-42 marks — You're nearly there — go back over the questions you found <u>tricky</u>.

43-50 marks — You're an <u>English whizz</u>.